BETTY BANDEL, lecturer, author, and teacher, is as much at home with books as she is strolling the campus of the University of Vermont, where she has been a prominent faculty member for 23 years. During this time her teaching activities have revolved around courses in creative writing, modern drama, Shakespeare, freshman composition, and English literature. She has written a novel, *Margaret Lane Cooper*, several plays, and numerous magazine articles. A member of many organizations, including the Shakespeare Association of America, the Vermont Historical Society, and the Modern Language Association, Dr. Bandel has found time to give lectures to community groups on such topics as the history of the position of women, Shakespeare, and the University of Vermont.

Dr. Bandel graduated from the University of Arizona with a degree in music and subsequently has received a master's degree and Ph.D. in English from Columbia University. Before teaching at the University of Vermont, she worked as a reporter and women's page editor for the *Arizona Daily Star* and during World War II served as a Lt. Colonel in the U.S. Army air forces for which she was awarded the Legion of Merit. Currently she is involved in writing and research for several articles.

WALK INTO MY PARLOR

Chapters from Inviting Books

WALK INTO MY PARLOR

Chapters from Inviting Books

compiled & edited by
BETTY BANDEL

CHARLES E. TUTTLE COMPANY
Rutland, Vermont & Tokyo, Japan

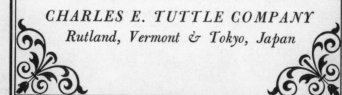

Representatives

For Continental Europe:
BOXERBOOKS, INC., *Zurich*

For the British Isles:
PRENTICE-HALL INTERNATIONAL, INC., *London*

For Australasia:
PAUL FLESCH & CO., PTY. LTD., *Melbourne*

For Canada:
M. G. HURTIG, LTD., *Edmonton*

Published by the Charles E. Tuttle Company, Inc.
of Rutland, Vermont & Tokyo, Japan
with editorial offices at
Suido 1-chome, 2-6, Bunkyo-ku, Tokyo

Copyright in Japan, 1972
by Charles E. Tuttle Co., Inc.

Library of Congress Catalog Card No. 76-158783
International Standard Book No. 0-8048-0920-8

First printing, 1972

Printed in Japan

TABLE OF CONTENTS

INTRODUCTION

It is difficult to refrain from extending the spider's invitation to the fly when one finds fellow readers who have not been entangled in the particular bookwebs to which one gladly submits. It is not that one wishes to dine on fellow readers, but rather that he hopes to share the feast, since, paradoxically, these webs are feasts.

This book is an invitation. It is an invitation to blow the figurative dust off a number of books in your town's library, and discover, or rediscover, much that is worth feasting on. In this day of "great books" lists, a book which was once quite popular but which has not taken its place among the enduring classics tends to disappear from view. Yet often it contains a more vivid picture of its times than does a book of more universal appeal. Also, it is likely to depict the day-to-day life of its time with special clarity. And, frequently, it tells a good story.

Included in this volume are chapters from a number

7

of books which were once popular. If you look up any one of them in your library, and if the library card stuck in at the back is old enough, you will discover that the book was checked out almost constantly for a good many years before 1914, sparingly during the Twenties, and sporadically since that time. It is hoped that none of the samples offered here is from a book of merely antiquarian interest. The stories range from the lightest summer reading to at least one classic, but they all share the interest that attaches to a genuinely good story. In the twentieth century, literary styles have changed as rapidly as all other styles, but today a re-examination is taking place in many fields of thought and endeavor which is emphasizing anew the ways in which we are like former generations of men, rather than the ways in which we differ from them. The question with regard to these books is not so much what change in literary fashion caused them to go out of style, but rather what wealth was lost when they did go out of style.

For one thing, an interestingly unmodern way of writing was lost. The figures of speech were drawn from a life which was keenly aware of each advancing day in the year's cycle of planting and harvesting and lasting out the winter. Qualifying phrases and clauses softened and added subtlety, instead of hammering at the main idea as if all thinking had to be done in headlines.

Another merit of these books which we can ill afford to lose is the picture they present of individual human beings living nineteenth century lives. Such portraits can do much to help us correct the black-and-white over-simplifications which we are especially prone to make about that part of history which is just back of our own times. See *Tom Brown at Oxford* for an unstereotyped Victorian father, and, for unstereotyped Puritans, *Oldtown Folks*.

Finally, these books, like many another from other times which is not today numbered among the "great books," contain part of the treasure of good writing which it is our privilege to store up and use. They contain vivid scenes and memorable events. If in addition many of them contain an attitude toward life which is foreign to us—and to which we attach the modern swearword *sentimental*—this fact should not prevent our finding their riches. No age was ever more bound by a fashion in thought than is our own, and we should sympathize. After all, the so-called "modern" in art was born seventy-five years ago, and soon an upstart generation will be pointing out that modern art is an old lady rustling in black taffeta.

John Milton was right. As good almost kill a man as kill a good book.

WALK INTO MY PARLOR

Chapters from Inviting Books

1. THE LONG VACATION LETTER-BAG

from *Tom Brown at Oxford* [Chapt. XXIX]
by Thomas Hughes, 1861

There is an old German fable about some young porcupines who were born one spring and spent much of the early summer tumbling and playing together, as the young of most species are inclined to do. One day in the late fall, after they had grown so independent and daring that each of them spent much of his time scampering and exploring alone, they felt the nip of the first really cold day they had known. They ran together for warmth and comfort, but, alas, their quills had grown stiff and strong during the summer. "Ouch!" said the outraged young porcupines, and "ouch" they repeated each time the cold drove them to repeat their experiment, until finally they appealed to their mother for a solution to their problems. "Ah, my dears," she said, "that is the secret of the good life—to stay close enough together to keep warm, yet not so close as to stick one another."

In an age in which too-anxious togetherness and too-

13

anxious separation cause trouble for both parents and children, it is interesting to note that not only an old German fable but also a mid-Victorian novel understood the delicate matter of keeping a proper distance in human relations. Tom Brown at Oxford, *not so famous as Thomas Hughes's story of Tom at Rugby,* Tom Brown's School Days, *is well worth reading not only for its account of a young man's growing up at Oxford a century ago but also for a picture of father-son relationships which runs counter to the stereotype of the stern, uncomprehending paterfamilias so often associated with Victorian life and literature. In the chapter given here, the elder Brown, Squire John Brown, wrestles with the problem of a chastened son whose first year at Oxford has brought him few triumphs and many problems. Tom has recklessly acted as co-signer of a note which two of the sporting set in college have used to raise additional funds for wine, women, and horses. The thing which Tom has not told his father, but feels he should confess, is that he has just avoided seducing a nice young barmaid in the nearby pub. It had been an eventful freshman year.*

Tom Brown, and Thomas Hughes, seem to have passed through Oxford without having been drawn into the religious and philosophic ferment which some of Dr. Thomas Arnold's disciples, including his own son Matthew, knew. But Dr. Arnold's influence on education was broad enough to affect not only the era's

*movements in thought, but also the move toward
"muscular Christianity" which made Tom Brown an
enthusiast for football and cricket at Rugby and for
boating at Oxford. It was also broad enough to endow
his disciples with deep social concern, so that Tom
Brown's discovery of Carlyle's* Past and Present *was the
one great intellectual excitement of his college career,
and so that Thomas Hughes in middle life could throw
all of his enthusiasm and most of his money into building a Rugby-ian cooperative colony for unemployed and
muscular English gentlemen in the uncooperative soil of
Tennessee. Rugby, Tenn., is still a dot on sufficiently
detailed maps.*

June 24, 184-

MY DEAR TOM: Your letter came to hand this morning, and it has of course given your mother and me
much pain. It is not the money that we care about, but
that our son should have deliberately undertaken, or
pretended to undertake, what he must have known at
the time he could not perform himself.

I have written to my bankers to pay £100 at once at
your account at the Oxford Bank. I have also requested
my solicitor to go over to Oxford, and he will probably
call on you the day after you receive this. You say that
this person who holds your note of hand is now in

Oxford. You will see him in the presence of my solicitor, to whom you will hand the note when you have recovered it. I shall consider afterward what further steps will have to be taken in the matter.

You will not be of age for a year. It will be time enough then to determine whether you will repay the balance of this money out of the legacy to which you will be entitled under your grandfather's will. In the meantime, I shall deduct at the rate of £50 a year from your allowance, and I shall hold you bound in honor to reduce your expenditure by this amount. You are no longer a boy, and one of the first duties which a man owes to his friends and to society is to live within his income.

I make this advance to you on two conditions. First, that you will never again put your hand to a note or bill in a transaction of this kind. If you have money, lend it or spend it. You may lend or spend foolishly, but that is not the point here; at any rate, you are dealing with what is your own. A gentleman should shrink from the possibility of having to come on others, even on his own father, for the fulfillment of his obligations as he would from a lie. I would sooner see a son of mine in his grave than crawling on through life a slave to wants and habits which he must gratify at other people's expense.

My second condition is, that you put an end to your acquaintance with these two gentlemen who have led you into this scrape, and have divided the proceeds of your joint note between them. They are both your seniors in standing, you say, and they appear to be familiar with this plan of raising money at the expense of other people. The plain English word for such doings is swindling. What pains me most is that you should have become intimate with young men of this kind. I am not sure that it will not be my duty to lay the whole matter before the authorities of the college. You do not mention their names, and I respect the feeling which has led you not to mention them. I shall know them quite soon enough through my solicitor, who will forward me a copy of the note of hand and signatures in due course.

Your letter makes general allusion to other matters; and I gather from it that you are dissatisfied with the manner in which you have spent your first year at Oxford. I do not ask for specific confessions, which you seem inclined to offer me; in fact, I would sooner not have them, unless there is any other matter in which you want assistance or advice from me. I know from experience that Oxford is a place full of temptation of all kinds, offered to young men at the most critical time of their lives. Knowing this, I have deliberately accepted the responsibility of sending you there, and I do not repent it. I am glad that you are dissatisfied with your first year. If you had not been, I should have felt much more anxious about your second. Let bygones be bygones between you and me. You know where to go for strength, and to make confessions which no human ear should hear, for no human judgment can weigh the cause. The secret places of a man's heart are for himself and God. Your mother sends her love.

I am, ever your affectionate father,
JOHN BROWN

*   *   *

June 26, 184-

MY DEAR BOY: I am not sorry that you have taken my last letter as you have done. It is quite right to be sensitive on these points, and it will have done you no harm to have fancied for forty-eight hours that you had in my judgment lost caste as a gentleman. But now I am very glad to be able to ease your mind on this point. You have done a very foolish thing; but it is only the habit, and the getting others to bind themselves, and not the doing it one's self for others, which is disgraceful. You are going to pay honorably for your folly, and will owe me neither thanks nor money in the transaction. I have chosen my own terms for repayment, which you have accepted, and so the financial question is disposed of.

I have considered what you say as to your companions—friends I will not call them—and will promise you not to take any further steps, or to mention the subject to anyone. But I must insist on my second condition, that you avoid all further intimacy with them. I do not mean that you are to cut them, or to do anything that will attract attention. But, no more intimacy.

And now, my dear boy, as to the rest of your letter. Mine must indeed have failed to express my meaning. God forbid that there should not be the most perfect confidence between us. There is nothing which I desire or value more. I only question whether special confessions will conduce to it. My experience is against them. I almost doubt whether they can be perfectly honest between man and man; and, taking into account the difference of our ages, it seems to me much more likely that we should misunderstand one another. But having said this, I leave it to you to follow your own conscience in the matter. If there is any burden which I can help you to bear, it will be my greatest pleasure, as it is my duty to do it. So now say what you please, or say no more. If you speak, it will be to one who has felt and remembers a young man's trials.

We hope you will be able to come home to-morrow, or the next day, at latest. Your mother is longing to see you, and I should be glad to have you here for a day or two before the assizes, which are held next week. I should rather like you to accompany me to them, as it will give me the opportunity of introducing you to my brother magistrates from other parts of the county, whom you are not likely to meet elsewhere, and it is a good thing for a young man to know his own county well.

The cricket club is flourishing, you will be glad to hear, and they have put off their best matches, especially those with the South Hants and Landsdown, till your return; so you are in great request, you see. I am told that the fishing is very good this year, and am promised several days for you in the club water.

September is a long way off, but there is nothing like being beforehand. I have put your name down for a license; and it is time you should have a good gun of your own; so I have ordered one for you from a man who has lately settled in the county. He was Purdy's foreman, with whom I used to build, and, I can see, understands his business thoroughly. His locks are as good as any I have ever seen. I have told him to make the stock rather longer, and not quite so straight as that of my old double with which you shot last year. I think I remember you criticised my weapon on these points; but there will be time for you to alter the details after you get home, if you disapprove of my orders. It will be more satisfactory if it is built under your own eye. If you continue in the mind for a month's reading with your friend Mr. Hardy, we will arrange it toward the end of vacation; but would he not come here? From what you say we should very much like to know him. Pray ask him from me whether he will pass the last month of the vacation here coaching you. I should like you to be his first regular pupil. Of course, this will be my affair. And now God bless you, and come home as soon as you can. Your mother sends her best love.

Ever your most affectionate
JOHN BROWN

2. LODGING AT MADRID...

from *The Bible in Spain* [Chapt. XII]
by George Borrow, 1842

*The modern small boy, seated comfortably on his
shoulderblades beside the driver of a whizzing auto-
mobile, sees, or senses, a remarkable number of above-
car-roof and below-car-door things. He is aware that it
was a Jaguar, not a Triumph, that just passed doing
eighty, and he is aware that the workmen in yellow
helmets at the corner of Main and McCormick were
taking down the signal lights, not climbing the tele-
phone pole. In the times when far and near were
measured in the distance a man could go on foot, or at
the best on horseback, in one day, people saw different
things. No matter how keen a modern man's vision is, he
will have missed a vast number of things that his great-
grandfather saw.*

*Probably what contributed as much as anything else
to the immediate success of George Borrow's* The Bible
in Spain, *when it appeared in 1842, was that George
Borrow saw a hundred things for every ten that the rest*

21

of our great-grandfathers' generation saw. Borrow had gone out to Spain in 1832 as the agent of the British and Foreign Bible Society to undertake the astonishing mission of selling Protestant Bibles in Catholic Spain. One thing Borrow could not see, or saw through a distorting glass: the Catholic Church. Edward Thomas, who wrote the introduction to the Everyman edition of The Bible in Spain, *says that "since Luther there has hardly been such a Protestant as Borrow." This one bit of myopia aside, Borrow saw with X-ray clarity. The result, as Thomas says, is "three fine things." The book "reveals part of a noble, brilliant, and friendly man." It "discovers to us a number of men and women (not to speak of the horses) . . . who jut out of the common level of life, our own life and the recorded past, like wrecks or crags at sea." It "creates a vast, difficult, sublime, romantic Spain for us." (The book makes a wonderful companion-piece to read alongside* Don Quixote, *as one discovers the life of the byways of Spain.)*

The very list of works by Borrow, whose speaking acquaintance with thirty-five languages got him his colporteur's job and the censure of some learned philologists, suggests his romantic leanings. The bibliography includes, among dozens of items, Targum, or Metrical Translations From Thirty Languages and Dialects; El Evangelio Segun S. Lucas, Traducido Al Romani; *and* The Sleeping Bard, *translated from The*

Cambrian British; *to say nothing of the better known* Gypsies *of Spain, Lavengro, and* The Romany Rye. *Anyone glancing down this list should be prepared for the fact that nobody has ever been able to decide where autobiography leaves off and fiction begins in a Borrow book, and also for the fact that Borrow ignores the Carlist wars and other facts of Spanish political life in the 1830's to bring the reader pictures of gypsies, jails, and ponies that remain brilliant when whole mosaics of dynasties have lost their glitter.*

In the chapter given here the young Spaniard, Baltasar, is described as a "national" ("nacional"). This is a term that was applied to citizen-soldiers, comparable to members of the National Guard in the United States. These troops were part of Queen Isabella the Second's defense against the reactionary Carlist party which wished to place Isabella's uncle, Don Carlos, on the throne of Spain. Baltasar refers contemptuously to the "Godos" (Goths), the reactionary young and idle members of the old gentry and nobility who, because of compulsory national military service, were being brought into military units previously made up of such liberal "nationals" as Baltasar himself.

It was the commencement of February when I reached Madrid. After staying a few days at a posada, I removed to a lodging which I engaged at No. 3, in the Calle de la Zarza, a dark dirty street, which, however, was close to the Puerta del Sol, the most central point of Madrid, into which four or five of the principal streets debouch, and which is, at all times of the year, the great place of assemblage for the idlers of the capital, poor or rich.

It was rather a singular house in which I had taken up my abode. I occupied the front part of the first floor; my apartments consisted of an immense parlour, and a small chamber on one side in which I slept; the parlour, notwithstanding its size, contained very little furniture: a few chairs, a table, and a species of sofa, constituted the whole. It was very cold and airy, owing to the draughts which poured in from three large windows, and from sundry doors. The mistress of the house, attended by her two daughters, ushered me in. "Did you ever see a more magnificent apartment?" demanded the former; "is it not fit for a king's son? Last winter it was occupied by the great General Espartero."

The hostess was an exceedingly fat woman, a native of Valladolid, in Old Castile. "Have you any other family," I demanded, "besides these daughters?" "Two sons," she replied; "one of them an officer in the army, father of this urchin," pointing to a wicked but clever-looking boy of about twelve, who at that moment bounded into the room; "the other is the most celebrated national in Madrid: he is a tailor by trade, and his name is Baltasar. He has much influence with the other nationals, on account of the liberality of his opinions, and a word from him is sufficient to bring them all out armed and furious to the Puerta del Sol. He is, however, at present confined to his bed, for he is very dissipated, and fond of the company of bull-fighters and people still worse."

As my principal motive for visiting the Spanish capital was the hope of obtaining permission from the government to print the New Testament in the Castilian language, for circulation in Spain, I lost no time, upon my arrival, in taking what I considered to be the necessary steps.

I was an entire stranger at Madrid, and bore no letters of introduction to any persons of influence, who might have assisted me in this undertaking, so that notwithstanding I entertained a hope of success, relying on the assistance of the Almighty, this hope was not at all times very vivid, but was frequently overcast with the clouds of despondency.

Mendizabal was at this time Prime minister of Spain, and was considered as a man of almost unbounded power, in whose hands were placed the destinies of the country. I therefore considered that if I could by any means induce him to favour my views, I should have no reason to fear interruption from other quarters, and I determined upon applying to him.

Before taking this step, however, I deemed it advisable to wait upon Mr. Villiers, the British ambassador at Madrid; and with the freedom permitted to a British subject, to ask his advice in this affair. I was received with great kindness, and enjoyed a conversation with him on various subjects before I introduced the matter which I had most at heart. He said that if I wished for an interview with Mendizabal, he would endeavour to procure me one, but, at the same time, told me frankly that he could not hope that any good would arise from it, as he knew him to be violently prejudiced against the British and Foreign Bible Society, and was far more likely to discountenance than encourage any efforts which they might be disposed to make for introducing the gospel into Spain. I, however, remained resolute in my desire to make the trial, and before I left him, obtained a letter of introduction to Mendizabal.

Early one morning I repaired to the palace, in a wing of which was the office of the Prime minister; it was bitterly cold, and the Guadarama, of which there is a noble view from the palace-plain, was covered with snow. For at least three hours I remained shivering with cold in an anteroom, with several other aspirants for an interview with the man of power. At last his private secretary made his appearance, and after putting various questions to the others, addressed himself to me, asking who I was and what I wanted. I told him that I was an Englishman, and the bearer of a letter from the British Minister. "If you have no objection, I will myself deliver it to His Excellency," said he; whereupon I handed it to him, and he withdrew. Several individuals were admitted before me; at last, however, my own turn came, and I was ushered into the presence of Mendizabal.

He stood behind a table covered with papers, on

which his eyes were intently fixed. He took not the slightest notice when I entered, and I had leisure enough to survey him: he was a huge athletic man, somewhat taller than myself, who measure six foot two without my shoes; his complexion was florid, his features fine and regular, his nose quite aquiline, and his teeth splendidly white; though scarcely fifty years of age, his hair was remarkably grey; he was dressed in a rich morning gown, with a gold chain round his neck, and morocco slippers on his feet.

His secretary, a fine intellectual-looking man, who, as I was subsequently informed, had acquired a name both in English and Spanish literature, stood at one end of the table with papers in his hands.

After I had been standing about a quarter of an hour, Mendizabal suddenly lifted up a pair of sharp eyes, and fixed them upon me with a peculiarly scrutinising glance.

"I have seen a glance very similar to that amongst the Beni Israel," thought I to myself. . . .

My interview with him lasted nearly an hour. Some singular discourse passed between us: I found him, as I had been informed, a bitter enemy to the Bible Society, of which he spoke in terms of hatred and contempt, and by no means a friend to the Christian religion, which I could easily account for. I was not discouraged, however, and pressed upon him the matter which brought me thither, and was eventually so far successful, as to obtain a promise, that at the expiration of a few months, when he hoped the country would be in a more tranquil state, I should be allowed to print the Scriptures.

As I was going away he said, "Yours is not the first application I have had: ever since I have held the reins of government I have been pestered in this manner by English calling themselves Evangelical Christians, who have of late come flocking over into Spain. Only last week a hunchbacked fellow found his way into my cabinet whilst I was engaged in important business, and told me that Christ was coming. . . . And now you have made your appearance, and almost persuaded me to embroil myself yet more with the priesthood, as if they did not abhor me enough already. What a strange infatuation is this which drives you over lands and waters with Bibles in your hands. My good sir, it is not Bibles we want, but rather guns and gunpower, to put the rebels down with, and above all, money, that we may pay the troops; whenever you come with these three things you shall have a hearty welcome; if not, we really can dispense with your visits, however great the honour."

Myself.—There will be no end to the troubles of this afflicted country until the gospel have free circulation.

Mendizabal.—I expected that answer, for I have not lived thirteen years in England without forming some acquaintance with the phraseology of you good folks. Now, now, pray go; you see how engaged I am. Come again whenever you please, but let it not be within the next three months.

"Don Jorge," said my hostess, coming into my apartment one morning, whilst I sat at breakfast with my feet upon the brasero, "here is my son Baltasarito, the national; he has risen from his bed, and hearing that there is an Englishman in the house, he has begged me to introduce him, for he loves Englishmen on account of the liberality of their opinions; there he is, what do you think of him?"

I did not state to his mother what I thought; it appeared to me, however, that she was quite right in calling him Baltasarito, which is the diminutive of Baltasar, forasmuch as that ancient and sonorous name had certainly never been bestowed on a more diminutive personage: he might measure about five feet one inch, though he was rather corpulent for his height; his face looked yellow and sickly, he had, however, a kind of fanfaronading air, and his eyes, which were of dark brown, were both sharp and brilliant. His dress, or rather his undress, was somewhat shabby: he had a foraging cap on his head, and in lieu of a morning gown, he wore a sentinel's old great-coat.

"I am glad to make your acquaintance, Señor nacional," said I to him, after his mother had departed, and Baltasar had taken a seat, and of course lighted a paper cigar at the brasero. "I am glad to have made your acquaintance, more especially as your lady mother has informed me that you have great influence with the nationals. I am a stranger in Spain, and may want a friend; fortune has been kind to me in procuring me one who is a member of so powerful a body."

Baltasar.—Yes, I have a great deal to say with the

other nationals; there is none in Madrid better known than Baltasar, or more dreaded by the Carlists. You say you may stand in need of a friend; there is no fear of my failing you in any emergency. Both myself and any of the other nationals will be proud to go out with you as padrinos, should you have any affair of honour on your hands. But why do you not become one of us? We would gladly receive you into our body.

Myself.—Is the duty of a national particularly hard?

Baltasar.—By no means; we have to do duty about once every fifteen days, and then there is occasionally a review, which does not last long. No! the duties of a national are by no means onerous, and the privileges are great. I have seen three of my brother nationals walk up and down the Prado of a Sunday, with sticks in their hands, cudgelling all the suspicious characters, and it is our common practice to scour the streets at night; and then if we meet any person who is obnoxious to us, we fall upon him, and with a knife or a bayonet generally leave him wallowing in his blood on the pavement: no one but a national would be permitted to do that.

Myself.—Of course none but persons of liberal opinions are to be found among the nationals?

Baltasar.—Would it were so! There are some amongst us, Don Jorge, who are no better than they should be; they are few, however, and for the most part well known. Theirs is no pleasant life, for when they mount guard with the rest they are scouted, and not unfrequently cudgelled. The law compels all of a certain age either to serve in the army or to become national soldiers, on which account some of these Godos are to be found amongst us.

Myself.—Are there many in Madrid of the Carlist opinion?

Baltasar.—Not among the young people; the greater part of the Madrilenian Carlists capable of bearing arms departed long ago to join the ranks of the factious in the Basque provinces. Those who remain are for the most part greybeards and priests, good for nothing but to assemble in private coffee-houses, and to prate treason together. Let them prate, Don Jorge; let them prate; the destinies of Spain do not depend on the wishes of ojalateros and pasteleros, but on the hands of stout gallant nationals like myself and friends, Don Jorge.

Myself.—I am sorry to learn from your lady mother that you are strangely dissipated.

Baltasar.—Ho, ho, Don Jorge! she has told you that, has she; what would you have, Don Jorge? I am young, and young blood will have its course. I am called Baltasar the gay by all the other nationals, and it is on account of my gaiety and the liberality of my opinions that I am so popular among them. When I mount guard I invariably carry my guitar with me, and then there is sure to be a funcion at the guard-house. We send for wine, Don Jorge, and the nationals become wild, Don Jorge, dancing and drinking through the night, whilst Baltasarito strums the guitar, and sings them songs of Germania,—

> *"Una romi sin pachi*
> *Le peno á su chindomar,"* etc., etc.

This is Gitáno, Don Jorge; I learnt it from the toreros of Andalusia, who all speak Gitáno, and are mostly of gipsy blood. I learnt it from them; they are all friends of mine, Montes Sevilla and Poquito Pan. I never miss a funcion of bulls, Don Jorge. Baltasar is sure to be there with his amiga. Don Jorge, there are no bull-funcions in the winter, or I would carry you to one, but happily to-morrow there is an execution, a funcion de la horca; and there we will go, Don Jorge.

We did go to see this execution, which I shall long remember. The criminals were two young men, brothers; they suffered for a most atrocious murder, having in the dead of night broke open the house of an aged man, whom they put to death, and whose property they stole. Criminals in Spain are not hanged as they are in England, or guillotined as in France, but strangled upon a wooden stage. They sit down on a kind of chair with a post behind, to which is affixed an iron collar with a screw; this iron collar is made to clasp the neck of the prisoner, and on a certain signal it is drawn tighter and tighter by means of the screw, until life becomes extinct. After we had waited amongst the assembled multitude a considerable time, the first of the culprits appeared; he was mounted on an ass, without saddle or stirrups, his legs being allowed to dangle nearly to the ground. He was dressed in yellow sulphur-coloured robes, with a high-peaked conical red hat on his head, which was shaven. Between his hands he held a parchment, on which was written something, I believe the confession of faith. Two priests led the animal by the bridle; two others walked on either side chanting litanies, amongst which I distinguished the words of heavenly peace and tranquillity, for the culprit had been reconciled to the Church, had confessed and received absolution, and had been promised admission to heaven. He did not exhibit the least symptom of fear, but dismounted from the animal and was led, not supported, up the scaffold, where he was placed on the chair, and the fatal collar put round his neck. One of the priests then in a loud voice commenced saying the Belief, and the culprit repeated the words after him. On a sudden, the executioner, who stood behind, commenced turning the screw, which was of prodigious force, and the wretched man was almost instantly a corpse; but, as the screw went round, the priest began to shout, *"Pax et misericordia et tranquillitas,"* and still as he shouted, his voice became louder and louder till the lofty walls of Madrid rang with it: then stooping down, he placed his mouth close to the culprit's ear, still shouting, just as if he would pursue the spirit through its course to eternity, cheering it on its way. The effect was tremendous. I myself was so excited that I involuntarily shouted *"misericordia,"* and so did many others. God was not thought of; Christ was not thought of; only the priest was thought of, for he seemed at that moment to be the first being in existence, and to have the power of opening and shutting the gates of heaven or of hell, just as he should think proper. A striking instance of the successful working of the Popish system, whose grand aim has ever been to keep people's minds as far as possible from God, and to centre their hopes and fears in the priesthood. The execution of the second culprit was precisely similar; he ascended the scaffold a few minutes after his brother had breathed his last.

I have visited most of the principal capitals of the world, but upon the whole none have ever so interested me as this city of Madrid, in which I now found myself. I will not dwell upon its streets, its edifices, its public squares, its fountains, though some of these are re-markable enough; but Petersburg has finer streets, Paris and Edinburgh more stately edifices, London far nobler squares, whilst Shiraz can boast of more costly fountains, though not cooler waters. But the popula-tion! Within a mud wall, scarcely one league and a half in circuit, are contained two hundred thousand human beings, certainly forming the most extraordinary vital mass to be found in the entire world; and be it always remembered that this mass is strictly Spanish. The population of Constantinople is extraordinary enough, but to form it twenty nations have contributed; Greeks, Armenians, Persians, Poles, Jews, the latter, by-the-bye, of Spanish origin, and speaking amongst themselves the old Spanish language; but the huge population of Madrid, with the exception of a sprinkling of foreigners, chiefly French tailors, glove-makers, and peruquiers, is strictly Spanish, though a considerable portion are not natives of the place. Here are no colonies of Germans, as at St. Petersburg; no English factories, as at Lisbon; no multitudes of insolent Yankees lounging through the streets, as at the Havannah, with an air which seems to say, the land is our own whenever we choose to take it; but a population which, however strange and wild, and composed of various elements, is Spanish, and will remain so as long as the city itself shall exist. Hail, ye aguadores of Asturia! who, in your dress of coarse duffel and leathern skull-caps, are seen seated in hundreds by the fountain sides, upon your empty water casks, or staggering with them filled to the topmost stories of lofty houses. Hail, ye caleseros of Valencia! who, lolling lazily against your vehicles, rasp tobacco for your paper cigars whilst waiting for a fare. Hail to you, beggars of La Mancha! men and women, who, wrapped in coarse blankets, demand charity indifferently at the gate of the palace or the prison. Hail to you, valets from the mountains, mayordomos and secretaries from Biscay and Guipuscoa, toreros from Andalusia, ripostos from Galicia, shopkeepers from Catalonia! Hail to ye, Castilians, Estremenians, and Aragonese, of whatever calling! And lastly, genuine sons of the capital, rabble of Madrid, ye twenty thousand manolos, whose terrible knives, on the second morning of May, worked such grim havoc amongst the legions of Murat!

And the higher orders — the ladies and gentlemen, the cavaliers and señoras; shall I pass them by in silence? The truth is I have little to say about them; I mingled but little in their society, and what I saw of them by no means tended to exalt them in my imagination. I am not one of those who, wherever they go, make it a constant practice to disparage the higher orders, and to exalt the populace at their expense. There are many capitals in which the high aristocracy, the lords and ladies, the sons and daughters of nobility, constitute the most remarkable and the most interesting part of the population. This is the case at Vienna, and more especially at London. Who can rival the English aristocrat in lofty stature, in dignified bearing, in strength of hand, and valour of heart? Who rides a nobler horse? Who has a firmer seat? And who more lovely than his wife, or sister, or daughter? But with respect to the Spanish aristocracy, the ladies and gentlemen, the cavaliers and señoras, I believe the less that is said of them on the points to which I have just alluded the better. I confess, however, that I know little about them; they have, perhaps, their admirers, and to the pens of such I leave their panegyric. Le Sage has described them as they were nearly two centuries ago. His description is anything but captivating, and I do not think that they have improved since the period of the sketches of the immortal Frenchman. I would sooner talk of the lower class, not only of Madrid but of all Spain. The Spaniard of the lower class has much more interest for me, whether manolo, labourer, or muleteer. He is not a common being; he is an extraordinary man. He has not, it is true, the amiability and generosity of the Russian mujik, nor his placid courage, which renders him insensible to fear, and at the command of his Tsar, sends him singing to certain death.* There is more hardness

* At the last attack on Warsaw, when the loss of the Russians amounted to upwards of twenty thousand men, the soldiery mounted the breach, repeating, in measured chant, one of their popular songs: "Come, let us cut the cabbage," etc. [Borrow's note]

and less self-devotion in the disposition of the Spaniard; he possesses, however, a spirit of proud independence, which it is impossible but to admire. He is ignorant, of course; but it is singular, that I have invariably found amongst the low and slightly educated classes far more liberality of sentiment than amongst the upper. It has long been the fashion to talk of the bigotry of the Spaniards, and their mean jealousy of foreigners. This is true to a certain extent; but it chiefly holds good with respect to the upper classes. If foreign valour or talent has never received its proper meed in Spain, the great body of the Spaniards are certainly not in fault. I have heard Wellington calumniated in this proud scene of his triumphs, but never by the old soldiers of Aragon and the Asturias, who assisted to vanquish the French at Salamanca and the Pyrenees. I have heard the manner of riding of an English jockey criticised, but it was by the idiotic heir of Medina Celi, and not by a picador of the Madrilenian bull ring.

Apropos of bull-fighters: Shortly after my arrival, I one day entered a low tavern in a neighbourhood notorious for robbery and murder, and in which for the last two hours I had been wandering on a voyage of discovery. I was fatigued, and required refreshment. I found the place thronged with people, who had all the appearance of ruffians. I saluted them, upon which they made way for me to the bar, taking off their sombreros with great ceremony. I emptied a glass of val de peñas, and was about to pay for it and depart, when a horrible-looking fellow, dressed in a buff jerkin, leather breeches, and jackboots, which came halfway up his thighs, and having on his head a white hat, the rims of which were at least a yard and a half in circumference, pushed through the crowd, and confronting me, roared,

"Otra copita! vamos Inglesito: Otra copita!"

"Thank you, my good sir, you are very kind, you appear to know me, but I have not the honour of knowing you."

"Not know me!" replied the being. "I am Sevilla, the torero. I know you well; you are the friend of Baltasarito, the national, who is a friend of mine, and a very good subject."

Then turning to the company, he said in a sonorous tone, laying a strong emphasis on the last syllable of every word, according to the custom of the gente rufianesca throughout Spain,--

"Cavaliers, and strong men, this cavalier is the friend of a friend of mine. *Es mucho hombre.* There is none like him in Spain. He speaks the crabbed Gitáno though he is an Inglesito."

"We do not believe it," replied several grave voices. "It is not possible."

"It is not possible, say you? I tell you it is. Come forward, Balseiro, you who have been in prison all your life, and are always boasting that you can speak the crabbed Gitáno, though I say you know nothing of it— come forward and speak to his worship in the crabbed Gitáno."

A low, slight, but active figure stepped forward. He was in his shirt sleeves, and wore a montero cap; his features were handsome, but they were those of a demon.

He spoke a few words in the broken gipsy slang of the prison, inquiring of me whether I had ever been in the condemned cell, and whether I knew what a Gitána* was?

"Vamos Inglesito," shouted Sevilla, in a voice of thunder; "answer the monro in the crabbed Gitáno."

I answered the robber, for such he was, and one, too, whose name will live for many a year in the ruffian histories of Madrid; I answered him in a speech of some length, in the dialect of the Estremenian gipsies.

"I believe it is the crabbed Gitáno," muttered Balseiro. "It is either that or English, for I understand not a word of it."

"Did I not say to you," cried the bull-fighter, "that you knew nothing of the crabbed Gitáno? But this Inglesito does. I understand all he said. Vaya, there is none like him for the crabbed Gitáno. He is a good ginete, too; next to myself, there is none like him, only he rides with stirrup leathers too short. Inglesito, if you have need of money, I will lend you my purse. All I have is at your service, and that is not a little; I have just gained four thousand chulés by the lottery. Courage, Englishman! Another cup. I will pay all. I, Sevilla!"

And he clapped his hand repeatedly on his breast, reiterating, "I, Sevilla! I ——"

* Twelve ounces of bread, small pound, as given in the prison. [Borrow's note]

3. THE GREAT WINTER

from *Lorna Doone* [Chapt. XIII]
by Richard Blackmore, 1869

The world owes Richard Doddridge Blackmore a debt of gratitude for abandoning the life of a lawyer and teacher for that of an orchardist and novelist. If he had not done so, the world would have been the poorer by the loss of Lorna Doone. *Surely the book is a classic of its kind, even if it is difficult to categorize. Strictly speaking, it is a historical romance; but Blackmore did well to call it simply "a romance of Exmoor," for it is the life of Exmoor, rather than the thread of history running through the tale, that provides its abiding charm. It is, as a man of Somerset once said to Blackmore, "as good as clotted cream, almost." Considering the fact that a number of their grandparents carried copies of "Lorna" in their coat pockets when they visited Somerset and Devon to look for "the Doone country," it is a shame that many well-read Americans under thirty have never encountered this old favorite.*

One can read the story for the adventures of "great

*John Ridd," whose ability to pull the muscle out of his
enemy's arm has caused some doctors to raise their
eyebrows. One can read it for John and Lorna's love
story. One can read it for the life of Exmoor. It is
probable that that life had changed little from the time
of the novel, the days of Charles the Second, to the time
of the novelist, the days of Victoria; or at any rate the
two eras were much closer together than the era of the
second Elizabeth is to either. Apartment-dwellers whose
greatest winter crisis is the failure of the thermostat that
governs the oil furnace could not do better than to
begin their exploration of* Lorna Doone *by living
through "the great winter" with John Ridd.*

It must have snowed most wonderfully to have made
that depth of covering in about eight hours. For one of
Master Stickles' men, who had been out all the night,
said that no snow began to fall until nearly midnight.
And there it was, blocking up the doors, stopping the
ways, and the water-courses, and making it very much
worse to walk than in a saw-pit newly used. However,
we trudged along in a line; I first, and the other men
after me; trying to keep my track, but finding legs and
strength not up to it. Most of all, John Fry was groaning; certain that his time was come, and sending
messages to his wife, and blessings to his children. For

all this time it was snowing harder than it ever had snowed before, so far as a man might guess at it; and the leaden depth of the sky came down, like a mine turned upside down on us. Not that the flakes were so very large; for I have seen much larger flakes in a shower of March, while sowing peas; but that there was no room between them, neither any relaxing, nor any change of direction.

Watch, like a good and faithful dog, followed us very cheerfully, leaping out of the depth, which took him over his back and ears already, even in the level places; while in the drifts he might have sunk to any distance out of sight, and never found his way up again. However, we helped him now and then, especially through the gaps and gate-ways; and so, after a deal of floundering, some laughter, and a little swearing, we came all safe to the lower meadow, where most of our flock was hurdled.

But behold, there was no flock at all! None, I mean, to be seen anywhere; only at one corner of the field, by the eastern end, where the snow drove in, a great white billow, as high as a barn and as broad as a house. This great drift was rolling and curling beneath the violent blast, tufting and combing with rustling swirls, and carved (as in patterns of cornice) where the grooving chisel of the wind swept round. Ever and again the tempest snatched little whiffs from the channeled edges, twirled them and made them dance over the chine of the monster pile, then let them lie like herring-bones, or the seams of sand where the tide has been. And all the while from the smothering sky, more and more fiercely at every blast, came the pelting, pitiless arrows, winged with murky white, and pointed with the barbs of frost.

But although, for people who had no sheep, the sight was a very fine one (so far, at least as the weather permitted any sight at all); yet for us, with our flock beneath it, this great mount had but little charm. Watch began to scratch at once, and to howl along the sides of it; he knew that his charge was buried there, and his business taken from him. But we four men set to in earnest, digging with all our might and main, shoveling away at the great white pile, and pitching it into the meadow. Each man made for himself a cave, scooping at the soft cold flux, which slid upon him at every stroke, and throwing it out behind him, in piles of castled fancy. At last we drove our tunnels in (for we worked indeed for the lives of us), and all converging toward the middle, held our tools and listened.

The other men heard nothing at all; or declared that they heard nothing, being anxious now to abandon the matter, because of the chill in their feet and knees. But I said, "Go, if you choose, all of you. I will work it out by myself, you pie-crusts!" and upon that they gripped their shovels, being more or less of Englishmen; and the least drop of English blood is worth the best of any other when it comes to lasting out.

But before we began again, I laid my head well into the chamber; and there I heard a faint "ma-a-ah," coming through some ells of snow, like a plaintive buried hope, or a last appeal. I shouted aloud to cheer him up, for I knew what sheep it was — to-wit, the most valiant of all the wethers, who had met me when I came home from London, and been so glad to see me. And then we all fell to again, and very soon we hauled him out. Watch took charge of him at once, with an air of the noblest patronage, lying on his frozen fleece, and licking all his face and feet, to restore his warmth to him. Then fighting Tom jumped up at once, and made a little butt at Watch, as if nothing had ever ailed him, and then set off to a shallow place, and looked for something to nibble at.

Further in, and close under the bank, where they had huddled themselves for warmth, we found all the rest of the poor sheep packed, as closely as if they were in a great pie. It was strange to observe how their vapor, and breath, and the moisture exuding from their wool, had scooped, as it were, a covered room for them, lined with a ribbing of deep yellow snow. Also the churned snow beneath their feet was as yellow as gamboge. Two or three of the weaklier hoggets were dead from want of air, and from pressure; but more than three-score were as lively as ever, though cramped and stiff for a little while.

"However shall us get 'em home?" John Fry asked, in great dismay, when we had cleared about a dozen of them; which we were forced to do very carefully, so as not to fetch the roof down. "No manner of maning to draive 'un, drough all they girt driftnesses."

"You see to this place, John," I replied, as we leaned on our shovels a moment, and the sheep came rubbing round us. "Let no more of them out for the present; they are better where they be. Watch! here, boy, keep them."

Watch came, with his little scut of a tail cocked as sharp as duty; and I set him at the narrow mouth of the great snow antre. All the sheep sidled away, and got closer, that the other sheep might be bitten first, as the foolish things imagine; whereas no good sheep-dog even so much as lips a sheep to turn it.

Then of the outer sheep (all now snowed and frizzled like a lawyer's wig) I took the two finest and heaviest, and with one beneath my right arm, and the other beneath my left, I went straight home to the upper sheppey, and set them inside, and fastened them. Sixty-and-six I took home in that way, two at a time on each journey; and the work grew harder and harder each time, as the drifts of the snow were deepening. No other man should meddle with them: I was resolved to try my strength against the strength of the elements; and try it I did, ay, and proved it. A certain fierce delight burned in me, as the struggle grew harder; but rather would I die than yield; and at last I finished it. People talk of it to this day; but none can tell what the labor was, who have not felt that snow and wind.

Of the sheep upon the mountain, and the sheep upon the western farm, and the cattle on the upper barrows, scarcely one in ten was saved, do what we would for them. And this was not through any neglect (now that our wits were sharpened), but from the pure impossibility of finding them at all. That great snow never ceased a moment for three days and nights; and then when all the earth was filled, and the topmost hedges were unseen, and the trees broke down with weight (wherever the wind had not lightened them), a brilliant sun broke forth and showed the loss of all our customs.

All our house was quite snowed up, except where we had purged a way by dint of constant shovelings. The kitchen was as dark, and darker, than the cider-cellar, and long lines of furrowed scollops ran even up to the chimney-stacks. Several windows fell right inward, through the weight of the snow against them; and the few that stood bulged in, and bent like an old bruised lantern. We were obliged to cook by candle-light; we were forced to read by candle-light; as for baking we could not do it, because the oven was too chill; and a load of fagots only brought a little wet down the sides of it.

For when the sun burst forth at last upon the world of white, what he brought was neither warmth, nor cheer, nor hope of softening; only a clearer shaft of cold, from the violent depths of sky. Long-drawn alleys of white haze seemed to lead toward him, yet such as he could not come down, with any warmth remaining. Broad white curtains of the frost-fog looped around the lower sky, on the verge of hill and valley, and above the laden trees. Only round the sun himself, and the spot of heaven he claimed, clustered a bright purple-blue, clear, and calm, and deep.

That night such a frost ensued as we had never dreamed of, neither read in ancient books, or histories

WAG

of Frobisher. The kettle by the fire froze, and the crock upon the hearth-cheeks; many men were killed, and cattle rigid in their head-ropes. Then I heard that fearful sound which never I had heard before, neither since have heard (except during that same winter), the sharp yet solemn sound of trees burst open by the frost-blow. Our great walnut lost three branches, and has been dying ever since; though growing meanwhile, as the soul does. And the ancient oak at the cross was rent, and many score of ash-trees. But why should I tell all this? The people who have not seen it (as I have) will only make faces, and disbelieve, till such another frost comes, which perhaps may never be.

This terrible weather kept Tom Faggus from coming near our house for weeks; at which, I was not vexed a quarter so much as Annie was; for I had never half approved of him as a husband for my sister, in spite of his purchase from Squire Bassett, and the grant of the royal pardon. It may be, however, that Annie took the same view of my love for Lorna, and could not augur well of it; but if so, she held her peace, though I was not so sparing. For many things contributed to make me less good-humored now than my real nature was; and the very least of all these things would have been enough to make some people cross, and rude, and fractious. I mean the red and painful chapping of my face and hands, from working in the snow all day, and lying in the frost all night. For being of a fair complexion, and a ruddy nature, and pretty plump withal, and fed on plenty of hot victuals, and always forced by my mother to sit nearer the fire than I wished, it was wonderful to see how the cold ran revel on my cheeks and knuckles. And I feared that Lorna (if it should ever please God to stop the snowing) might take this for a proof of low and rustic blood and breeding.

And this, I say, was the smallest thing; for it was far more serious that we were losing half our stock, do all we would to shelter them. Even the horses in the stables (mustered altogether, for the sake of breath and steaming) had long icicles from their muzzles, almost every morning. But of all things the very gravest, to my apprehension, was the impossibility of hearing, or having any token, of or from my loved one. Not that those three days alone of snow (tremendous as it was) could have blocked the country so; but that the sky had never ceased, for more than two days at a time, for full three weeks thereafter, to pour fresh piles of fleecy mantle; neither had the wind relaxed a single day from shaking them. As a rule, it snowed all day, cleared up at night, and froze intensely, with the stars as bright as jewels, earth spread out in lustrous twilight, and the sounds in the air as sharp and crackling as artillery, then in the morning snow again, before the sun could come to help.

It mattered not what way the wind was. Often and often the vanes went round, and we hoped for change of weather: the only change was that it seemed (if possible) to grow colder. Indeed, after a week or so, the wind would regularly box the compass (as the sailors call it) in the course of every day, following where the sun should be, as if to make a mock of him. And this, of course, immensely added to the peril of the drifts; because they shifted every day, and no skill or care might learn them.

I believe it was on Epiphany morning, or somewhere about that period, when Lizzie ran into the kitchen to me, where I was thawing my goose-grease, with the dogs among the ashes — the live dogs, I mean, not the iron ones, for them we had given up long ago — and having caught me, by way of wonder (for generally I was out shoveling long before my "young lady" had her night-cap off), she positively kissed me, for the sake of warming her lips, perhaps, or because she had something proud to say.

"You great fool, John," said my lady, as Annie and I used to call her, on account of her airs and graces; "what a pity you never read, John!"

"Much use, I should think, in reading!" I answered, though pleased with her condescension; "read, I suppose, with roof coming in, and only this chimney left sticking out of the snow!"

"The very time to read, John," said Lizzie, looking grander; "our worst troubles are the need, whence knowledge can deliver us."

"Amen!" I cried out; "are you parson or clerk? Whichever you are, good-morning."

Thereupon I was bent on my usual round (a very small one nowadays), but Eliza took me with both hands, and I stopped of course; for I could not bear to shake the child, even in play, for a moment, because her back was tender. Then she looked up at me with her beautiful eyes, so large, unhealthy, and delicate, and strangely shadowing outward, as if to spread their meaning; and she said:

"Now, John, this is no time to joke. I was almost frozen in bed last night; and Annie like an icicle. Feel how cold my hands are. Now, will you listen to what I have to read about climates ten times worse than this; and where none but clever men can live?"

"Impossible for me to listen now. I have hundreds of things to see to; but I will listen after breakfast to your foreign climate, child. Now attend to mother's hot coffee."

She looked a little disappointed, but she knew what I had to do; and after all she was not so utterly unreasonable, although she did read books. And when I had done my morning's work, I listened to her patiently; and it was out of my power to think that all she said was foolish.

For I knew common sense pretty well by this time, whether it happened to be my own or any other person's, if clearly laid before me. And Lizzie had a particular way of setting forth very clearly whatever she wished to express and enforce. But the queerest part of it all was this: That if she could but have dreamed for a moment what would be the first application made by me of her lesson, she would rather have bitten her tongue off than help me to my purpose.

She told me that in the "Arctic Regions," as they call some places a long way north, where the great bear lies across the heavens, and no sun is up for whole months at a time, and yet where people will go exploring, out of pure contradiction, and for the sake of novelty, and love of being frozen — that here they always had such winters as we were having now. It never ceased to freeze, she said, and it never ceased to snow, except when it was too cold; and then all the air was choked with glittering spikes, and a man's skin might come off of him before he could ask the reason. Nevertheless, the people there (although the snow was fifty feet deep and all their breath fell behind them frozen, like a log of wood dropped from their shoulders) managed to get along and make the time of the year to each other, by a little cleverness. For seeing how the snow was spreading lightly over everything, covering up the hills and valleys, and the foreskin of the sea, they contrived a way to crown it, and to glide like a flake along. Through the sparkle of the whiteness, and the wreathes of windy tossings, and the ups and downs of cold, any man might get along with a boat on either foot to prevent his sinking.

She told me how these boats were made; very strong and very light, of ribs of skin across them; five feet long and one foot wide, and turned up at each end, even as a canoe is. But she did not tell me, nor did I give a moment's thought myself, how hard it was to walk upon them without early practice. Then she told me another thing equally useful to me; although I would not let her see how much I thought about it. And this concerned the use of sledges, and their power of gliding, and the lightness of their following; all of which I could see at once, through knowledge of our farm sleds, which we employ in lieu of wheels, used in flatter districts. When I had heard all this from her, a mere chit of a girl as she was, unfit to make a snowball even, or to fry snow-pancakes, I looked down on her with amazement, and began to wish a little that I had given more time to books.

But God shapes all our fitness, and gives each man his meaning, even as he guides the wavering lines of snow descending. Our Eliza was meant for books; our dear Annie for loving and cooking; I, John Ridd, for sheep, and wrestling, and the thought of Lorna; and mother to love all three of us, and to make the best of her children. And now, if I must tell the truth, as at every page I try to do (though God knows it is hard enough), I had felt through all this weather, though my life was Lorna's, something of a satisfaction in so doing duty to my kindest and best of mothers, and to none but her. For (if you come to think of it) a man's young love is very pleasant, very sweet and tickling, and takes him through the core of heart, without his knowing how or why. Then he dwells upon it sideways, without people looking, and builds up all sorts of fancies, growing hot with working at his own imaginings. So his love is a crystal goddess, set upon an obelisk; and whoever will not bow the knee (yet without glancing at her), the lover makes it a sacred rite either to kick or to stick him. I am not speaking of me and Lorna, but of common people.

Then (if you come to think of it again) lo — or I will not say lo! for no one can behold it — only feel, or but remember, what a real mother is. Ever loving, ever soft, ever turning sin to goodness, vices into virtues; blind to all nine-tenths of wrong; through a telescope beholding (though herself so nigh to them) faintest decimal of promise, even in her vilest child. Ready to thank God again, as when her babe was born to her; leaping (as at kingdom come) at a wandering syllable of Gospel for her lost one.

All this our mother was to us, and even more than all of this; and hence I felt a pride and joy in doing my sacred duty toward her, now that the weather compelled me. And she was as grateful and delighted as if she had no more claim upon me than a stranger's sheep might have. Yet from time to time I groaned within myself and by myself at thinking of my sad debarment from the sight of Lorna, and of all that might have happened to her, now she had no protection.

Therefore I fell to at once, upon that hint from Lizzie; and being used to thatching-work, and the making of traps, and so on, before very long I built myself a pair of strong and light snow-shoes, framed with ash and ribbed of withy, with half-tanned calfskin stretched across, and an inner sole to support my feet. At first I could not walk at all, but floundered about most piteously, catching one shoe in the other, and both of them in the snow-drifts, to the great amusement of the girls, who were come to look at me. But after a while I grew more expert, discovering what my errors

were, and altering the inclination of the shoes themselves according to a print which Lizzie found in a book
of adventures. And this made such a difference, that I
crossed the farm-yard and came back again (though
turning was the worst thing of all) without so much as
falling once, or getting my staff entangled.

But oh, the aching of my ankles when I went to bed
at night! I was forced to help myself upstairs with a
couple of mop-sticks; and I rubbed the joints with neats-
foot oil, which comforted them greatly. And likely
enough I would have abandoned any further trial, but
for Lizzie's ridicule and pretended sympathy, asking if
the strong John Ridd would have old Betty to lean
upon. Therefore I set to again, with a fixed resolve not
to notice pain or stiffness, but warm them out of me.
And sure enough before dark that day I could get along
pretty freely: especially improving every time, after
leaving off and resting. The astonishment of poor John
Fry, Bill Dadds and Jem Slocombe, when they saw me
coming down the hill upon them in the twilight, where
they were clearing the furze-rick and trussing it for
cattle, was more than I can tell you; because they did
not let me see it, but ran away with one accord, and
floundered into a snow-drift. They believed, and so did
every one else (especially when I grew able to glide
pretty rapidly), that I had stolen Mother Melldrum's
sieves, on which she was said to fly over the foreland at
midnight every Saturday.

Upon the following day I held some council with my
mother; not liking to go without her permission, yet

scarcely daring to ask for it. But here she disappointed
me, on the right side of disappointment; saying that she
had seen my pining (which she never could have done,
because I had been too hard at work), and rather than
watch me grieving so for somebody or other who now
was all in all to me, I might go upon my course, and
God's protection go with me! At this I was amazed,
because it was not at all like mother; and knowing how
well I had behaved ever since the time of our snowing
up, I was a little moved to tell her that she could not
understand me. However, my sense of duty kept me,
and my knowledge of the catechism, from saying such a
thing as that, or even thinking twice of it. And so I took
her at her word, which she was not prepared for; and
telling her how proud I was of her trust in Providence,
and how I could run in my new snow-shoes, I took a
short pipe in my mouth, and started forth accordingly.

4. THE SHEPHERDS' TROPHY

from *Bob, Son of Battle* [Chapt. XXV]
by Alfred Ollivant, 1898

Never was the pathetic fallacy put to better use than in Ollivant's Bob, Son of Battle. *The dogs, as protagonists and antagonists of the tale, think like people and act like dogs; and the result is two stories for the price of one — two kinds of heroism and two kinds of villainy. In the end the dogs even gang up and plan the murder, or rather execution, of the villain-dog.*

So successful did this formula prove that Ollivant, who had turned to writing after giving up his career in the British army because of an injury, found himself the author of an immensely successful book, and youngsters during the first two decades of the twentieth century discovered as many as three copies of Bob *in their Christmas stockings. It was no good trying to trade two, because everyone else on the block had also gotten at least one.*

The story has many riches, among them a villain-dog, Red Wull, who frequently steals the spotlight from the

*hero, Owd Bob; and a man, M'Adam, owner of Red
Wull, whose portrayal as the "different" one in a tight
little community is remarkable. Nothing in the tale is
more arresting, however, than the descriptions of the
sheep-herding dogs of northern England and Scotland at
their work. This aspect of the story reaches its climax in
the chapter, "The Shepherds' Trophy," when Owd Bob
attempts to do what no other dog has ever done —
capture the Champion Challenge Dale Cup, awarded at
the annual sheepdog trials, for the third time, and thus
bring it into the permanent possession of his master.
Not the least interesting element in the chapter is Red
Wull's magnificent showing, the judges' final decision,
and M'Adam's suspicion — how many readers share it?
— that prejudice had something to do with the selection
of the winner.*

Cup Day.

It broke calm and beautiful, no cloud on the horizon,
no threat of storm in the air; a fitting day on which the
Shepherds' Trophy must be won outright.

And well it was so. For never since the founding of
the Dale Trials had such a concourse been gathered
together on the north bank of the Silver Lea. From the
Highlands they came; from the far Campbell country;
from the Peak; from the county of many acres; from all

along the silver fringes of the Solway; assembling in that quiet corner of the earth to see the famous Gray Dog of Kenmuir fight his last great battle for the Shepherds' Trophy.

By noon the gaunt Scaur looked down on such a gathering as it had never seen. The paddock at the back of the Dalesman's Daughter was packed with a clammering, chattering multitude: animated groups of farmers; bevies of solid rustics; sharp-faced townsmen; loud-voiced bookmakers; giggling girls; amorous boys, — thrown together like toys in a sawdust bath; whilst here and there on the outskirts of the crowd, a lonely man and wise-faced dog, come from afar to wrest his proud title from the best sheep-dog in the North.

At the back of the enclosure was drawn up a formidable array of carts and carriages, varying as much in quality and character as did their owners. There was the squire's landau rubbing axle-boxes with Jem Burton's modest moke-cart; and there Viscount Birdseye's flaring barouche side by side with the red-wheeled wagon of Kenmuir.

In the latter, Maggie, sad and sweet in her simple summer garb, leant over to talk to Lady Eleanour; while golden-haired wee Anne, delighted with the surging crowd around, trotted about the wagon, waving to her friends, and shouting from very joyousness.

Thick as flies clustered that motley assembly on the north bank of the Silver Lea. While on the other side of the stream was a little group of judges, inspecting the course.

The line laid out ran thus: the sheep must first be found in the big enclosure to the right of the starting flag; then up the slope and away from the spectators; around a flag and obliquely down the hill again; through a gap in the wall; along the hillside, parallel to the Silver Lea; abruptly to the left through a pair of flags — the trickiest turn of them all; then down the slope to the pen, which was set up close to the bridge over the stream.

The proceedings began with the Local Stakes, won by Rob Saunderson's veteran, Shep. There followed the Open Juveniles, carried off by Ned Hoppin's young dog. It was late in the afternoon when, at length, the great event of the meeting was reached.

In the enclosure behind the Dalesman's Daughter the clamour of the crowd increased tenfold, and the yells of the bookmakers were redoubled.

"Walk up, gen'lemen, walk up! the ole firm! Rasper? Yessir — twenty to one bar two! Twenty to one bar two! Bob? What price, Bob? Even money, sir — no, not a penny longer, couldn't do it! Red Wull? 'oo says Red Wull?"

On the far side of the stream is clustered about the starting flag the finest array of sheep-dogs ever seen together.

"I've never seen such a field, and I've seen fifty," is Parson Leggy's verdict.

There, beside the tall form of his master, stands Owd Bob o' Kenmuir, the observed of all. His silvery brush fans the air, and he holds his dark head high as he scans his challengers, proudly conscious that to-day will make or mar his fame. Below him, the mean-looking, smooth-coated black dog is the unbeaten Pip, winner of the renowned Cambrian Stakes at Llangollen – as many think the best of all the good dogs that have come from sheep-dotted Wales. Beside him that sable collie, with the tremendous coat and slash of white on throat and face, is the famous MacCallum More, fresh from his victory at the Highland meeting. The cobby, brown dog, seeming of many breeds, is from the land o' the Tykes – Merry, on whom the Yorkshiremen are laying as though they loved him. And Jess, the wiry black-and-tan, is the favourite of the men of the Derwent and Dove. Tupper's big blue Rasper is there; Londesley's Lassie; and many more – too many to mention: big and small, grand and mean, smooth and rough – and not a bad dog there.

And alone, his back to the others, stands a little bowed, conspicuous figure – Adam M'Adam; while the great dog beside him, a hideous incarnation of scowling defiance, is Red Wull, the Terror o' the Border.

The Tailless Tyke had already run up his fighting colours. For MacCallum More, going up to examine this forlorn great adversary, had conceived for him a violent antipathy, and, straightway, had spun at him with all the fury of the Highland cateran, who attacks first and explains afterward. Red Wull, forthwith, had turned on him with savage, silent gluttony; bob-tailed Rasper was racing up to join in the attack; and in another second the three would have been locked inseparably – but just in time M'Adam intervened.

One of the judges came hurrying up.

"Mr. M'Adam," he cried angrily, "if that brute of yours gets fighting again, hang me if I don't disqualify him! Only last year at the Trials he killed the young Cossack dog."

A dull flash of passion swept across M'Adam's face. "Come here, Wullie!" he called. "Gin yon Hielant tyke attacks ye agin, ye're to be disqualified."

He was unheeded. The battle for the Cup had begun — little Pip leading the dance.

On the opposite slope the babel had subsided now. Hucksters left their wares, and bookmakers their stools, to watch the struggle. Every eye was intent on the moving figures of man and dog and three sheep over the stream.

One after one the competitors ran their course and penned their sheep — there was no single failure. And all received their just meed of applause, save only Adam M'Adam's Red Wull.

Last of all, when Owd Bob trotted out to uphold his title, there went up such a shout as made Maggie's wan cheeks to blush with pleasure, and wee Anne to scream right lustily.

His was an incomparable exhibition. Sheep should be humoured rather than hurried; coaxed rather than coerced. And that sheep-dog has attained the summit of his art who subdues his own personality and leads his sheep in pretending to be led. Well might the bosoms of the Dalesmen swell with pride as they watched their favourite at his work; well might Tammas pull out that hackneyed phrase, "The brains of a mon and the way of a woman"; well might the crowd bawl their enthusiasm, and Long Kirby puff his cheeks and rattle the money in his trouser pockets.

But of this part it is enough to say that Pip, Owd Bob, and Red Wull were selected to fight out the struggle afresh.

*   *   *

The course was altered and stiffened. On the far side the stream it remained as before; up the slope; round a flag, down the hill again; through the gap in the wall; along the hillside; down through the two flags; turn; and to the stream again. But the pen was removed from its former position, carried over the bridge, up the near slope, and the hurdles put together at the very foot of the spectators.

The sheep had to be driven over the plank-bridge, and the penning done beneath the very nose of the crowd. A stiff course, if ever there was one; and the time allowed, ten short minutes.

*   *   *

The spectators hustled and elbowed in their endeavours to obtain a good position. And well they might; for about to begin was the finest exhibition of sheep-handling any man there was ever to behold.

*   *   *

Evan Jones and little Pip led off.

Those two, who had won on many a hard-fought field, worked together as they had never worked before. Smooth and swift, like a yacht in Southampton Water; round the flag, through the gap, they brought their sheep. Down between the two flags — accomplishing right well that awkward turn; and back to the bridge.

There they stopped: the sheep would not face that narrow way. Once, twice, and again, they broke; and each time the gallant little Pip, his tongue out and tail quivering, brought them back to the bridge-head.

At length one faced it; then another, and — it was too late. Time was up. The judges signalled; and the Welshman called off his dog and withdrew.

Out of sight of mortal eye, in a dip of the ground, Evan Jones sat down and took the small dark head between his knees — and you may be sure the dog's heart was heavy as the man's. "We did our pest, Pip," he cried brokenly, "but we're peat — the first time ever we've been!"

*   *   *

No time to dally.

James Moore and Owd Bob were off on their last run.

No applause this time; not a voice was raised; anxious faces; twitching fingers; the whole crowd tense as a stretched wire. A false turn, a wilful sheep, a cantankerous judge, and the gray dog would be beat. And not a man there but knew it.

Yet over the stream master and dog went about their business never so quiet, never so collected; for all the world as though they were rounding up a flock on the Muir Pike.

The old dog found his sheep in a twinkling and a wild, scared trio they proved. Rounding the first flag, one bright-eyed wether made a dash for the open. He was quick; but the gray dog was quicker: a splendid recover, and a sound like a sob from the watchers on the hill.

Down the slope they came for the gap in the wall. A little below the opening, James Moore took his stand to stop and turn them; while a distance behind his sheep loitered Owd Bob, seeming to follow rather than drive, yet watchful of every movement and anticipating it. On he came, one eye on his master, the other on his sheep; never hurrying them, never flurrying them, yet bringing them rapidly along.

No word was spoken; barely a gesture made; yet they worked, master and dog, like one divided.

Through the gap, along the hill parallel to the spectators, playing into one another's hands like men at polo.

A wide sweep for the turn at the flags, and the sheep wheeled as though at the word of command, dropped through them, and travelled rapidly for the bridge.

"Steady!" whispered the crowd.

"Steady, man!" muttered Parson Leggy.

"Hold 'em, for God's sake!" croaked Kirby huskily. "D—n! I knew it! I saw it coming!"

The pace down the hill had grown quicker — too quick. Close on the bridge the three sheep made an effort to break. A dash — and two were checked; but the third went away like the wind, and after him Owd Bob, a gray streak against the green.

Tammas was cursing silently; Kirby was white to the lips; and in the stillness you could plainly hear the Dalesmen's sobbing breath, as it fluttered in their throats.

"Gallop! they say he's old and slow!" muttered the Parson. "Dash! Look at that!" For the gray dog, racing like the nor'easter over the sea, had already retrieved the fugitive.

Man and dog were coaxing the three a step at a time toward the bridge.

One ventured — the others followed.

In the middle the leader stopped and tried to turn — and time was flying, flying, and the penning alone must take minutes. Many a man's hand was at his watch, but no one could take his eyes off the group below him to look.

"We're beat! I've won bet, Tammas!" groaned Sam'l. (The two had a long-standing wager on the matter.) "I allus knoo hoo 'twould be. I allus told yo' th' owd tyke —" Then breaking into a bellow, his honest face crimson with enthusiasm: "Come on, Master! Good for yo', Owd Un! Yon's the style!"

For the gray dog had leapt on the back of the hindmost sheep; it had surged forward against the next, and they were over, and making up the slope amidst a thunder of applause.

At the pen it was a sight to see shepherd and dog working together. The Master, his face stern and a little whiter than its wont, casting forward with both hands, herding the sheep in; the gray dog, his eyes big and bright, dropping to hand; crawling and creeping, closer and closer

"They're in! — Nay — Ay — dang me! Stop 'er. Good Owd Un! Ah-h-h, they're in!" And the last sheep reluctantly passed through — on the stroke of time.

A roar went up from the crowd; Maggie's white face turned pink; and the Dalesmen mopped their wet brows. The mob surged forward, but the stewards held them back.

"Back, please! Don't encroach! M'Adam's to come!"

From the far bank the little man watched the scene. His coat and cap were off, and his hair gleamed white in the sun; his sleeves were rolled up; and his face was twitching but set as he stood — ready.

The hubbub over the stream at length subsided. One of the judges nodded to him.

"Noo, Wullie — noo or niver! — 'Scots wha hae'!" — and they were off.

"Back, gentlemen! Back! He's off — he's coming. M'Adam's coming!"

They might well shout and push; for the great dog was on to his sheep before they knew it; and they went away with a rush, with him right on their backs. Up the slope they swept and round the first flag, already galloping. Down the hill for the gap, and M'Adam was flying ahead to turn them. But they passed him like a hurricane, and Red Wull was in front with a rush and turned them alone.

"M'Adam wins! Five to four M'Adam! I lay agin Owd Bob!" rang out a clear voice in the silence.

Through the gap they rattled, ears back, feet twinkling like the wings of driven grouse.

"He's lost 'em! They'll break! They're away!" was the cry.

Sam'l was half up the wheel of the Kenmuir wagon; every man was on his toes; ladies were standing in their carriages; even Jim Mason's face flushed with momentary excitement.

The sheep were tearing along the hillside, all together, like a white scud. After them, galloping like a Waterloo winner, raced Red Wull. And last of all, leaping over the ground like a demoniac, making not for the two flags, but the plankbridge, the white-haired figure of M'Adam.

"He's beat! The Killer's beat!" roared a strident voice.

"M'Adam wins! Five to four M'Adam! I lay agin Owd Bob!" rang out the clear reply.

Red Wull was now racing parallel to the fugitives and above them. All four were travelling at a terrific rate; while the two flags were barely twenty yards in front, below the line of flight and almost parallel to it. To effect the turn a change of direction must be made almost through a right angle.

"He's beat! he's beat! M'Adam's beat! Can't make it nohow!" was the roar.

From over the stream a yell —

"Turn 'em, Wullie!"

At the word the great dog swerved down on the

flying three. They turned, still at the gallop, like a troop of cavalry, and dropped, clean and neat, between the flags; and down to the stream they rattled, passing M'Adam on the way as though he was standing.

"Weel done, Wullie!" came the scream from the far bank; and from the crowd went up an involuntary burst of applause.

"Ma word!"

"Did yo' see that?"

"By gob!"

It was a turn, indeed, of which the smartest team in the galloping horsegunners might well have been proud. A shade later, and they must have overshot the mark; a shade sooner, and a miss.

"He's not been two minutes so far. We're beaten — don't you think so, Uncle Leggy?" asked Muriel Sylvester, looking up piteously into the parson's face.

"It's not what I think, my dear; it's what the judges think," the parson replied; and what he thought their verdict would be was plainly writ on his face for all to read.

Right on to the centre of the bridge the leading sheep galloped and — stopped abruptly.

Up above in the crowd there was utter silence; staring eyes; rigid fingers. The sweat was dripping off Long Kirby's face; and, at the back, a green-coated book-maker slipped his notebook in his pocket, and glanced behind him. James Moore, standing in front of them all, was the calmest there.

Red Wull was not to be denied. Like his forerunner

he leapt on the back of the hindmost sheep. But the red dog was heavy where the gray was light. The sheep staggered, slipped, and fell.

Almost before it had touched the water, M'Adam, his face afire and eyes flaming, was in the stream. In a second he had hold of the struggling creature, and, with an almost superhuman effort, had half thrown, half shoved it on to the bank.

Again a tribute of admiration, led by James Moore.

The little man scrambled, panting, on to the bank and raced after sheep and dog. His face was white beneath the perspiration; his breath came in quavering gasps; his trousers were wet and clinging to his legs; he was trembling in every limb, and yet indomitable.

They were up to the pen, and the last wrestle began. The crowd, silent and motionless, craned forward to watch the uncanny, white-haired little man and the huge dog, working so close below them. M'Adam's face was white; his eyes staring, unnaturally bright; his bent body projected forward; and he tapped with his stick on the ground like a blind man, coaxing the sheep in. And the Tailless Tyke, his tongue out and flanks heaving, crept and crawled and worked up to the opening, patient as he had never been before.

They were in at last.

There was a lukewarm, half-hearted cheer; then silence.

Exhausted and trembling, the little man leant against the pen, one hand on it; while Red Wull, his flanks still heaving, gently licked the other. Quite close stood

James Moore and the gray dog; above was the black wall of people, utterly still; below, the judges comparing notes. In the silence you could almost hear the panting of the crowd.

Then one of the judges went up to James Moore and shook him by the hand.

The gray dog had won. Owd Bob o' Kenmuir had won the Shepherds' Trophy outright.

A second's palpitating silence; a woman's hysterical laugh — and a deep-mouthed bellow rent the expectant air: shouts, screams, hat-tossings, back-clappings blending in a din that made the many-winding waters of the Silver Lea quiver and quiver again.

Owd Bob o' Kenmuir had won the Shepherds' Trophy outright.

Maggie's face flushed a scarlet hue. Wee Anne flung fat arms around her triumphant Bob, and screamed with the best. Squire and parson, each red-cheeked, were boisterously shaking hands. Long Kirby, who had not prayed for thirty years, ejaculated with heartfelt earnestness, "Thank God!" Sam'l Todd bellowed in Tammas's ear, and almost slew him with his mighty buffets. Among the Dalesmen some laughed like drunken men; some cried like children; all joined in that roaring song of victory.

To little M'Adam, standing with his back to the crowd, that storm of cheering came as the first announcement of defeat.

A wintry smile, like the sun over a March sea, crept across his face.

"We might a kent it, Wullie," he muttered, soft and low. The tension loosed, the battle lost, the little man almost broke down. There were red dabs of colour in his face; his eyes were big; his lips pitifully quivering; he was near to sobbing.

An old man — utterly alone — he had staked his all on a throw — and lost.

Lady Eleanour marked the forlorn little figure, standing solitary on the fringe of the uproarious mob. She noticed the expression on his face; and her tender heart went out to the lone man in his defeat.

She went up to him and laid a hand upon his arm.

"Mr. M'Adam," she said timidly, "won't you come and sit down in the tent? You look so tired! I can find you a corner where no one shall disturb you."

The little man wrenched roughly away. The unexpected kindness, coming at that moment, was almost too much for him. A few paces off he turned again.

"It's reel kind o' yer ladyship," he said huskily; and tottered away to be alone with Red Wull.

*   *   *

Meanwhile the victors stood like rocks in the tideway. About them surged a continually changing throng, shaking the man's hand, patting his dog.

Maggie had carried wee Anne to tender her congratulations; Long Kirby had come; Tammas, Saunderson, Hoppin, Tupper, Londesley — all but Jim Mason; and now, elbowing through the press, came squire and parson.

"Well done, James! well done, indeed! Knew you'd win! Told you so — oh, eh!" Then facetiously to Owd Bob: "Knew you would, Robert, old man! Ought to — Robert the Dev — musn't be a naughty boy — eh, eh!"

The first time ever the Dale Cup's been won outright!" said the parson; "and I dare say it never will again. And I think Kenmuir's the very fittest place for its final home, and a Gray Dog of Kenmuir for its winner."

"Oh, by the by!" burst in the squire. "I've fixed the Manor dinner for to-day fortnight, James. Tell Saunderson and Tupper, will you? Want all the tenants there." He disappeared into the crowd, but in a minute had fought his way back. "I'd forgotten something!" he shouted. "Tell your Maggie perhaps you'll have news for her after it — ey! eh!" — and he was gone again.

Last of all, James Moore was aware of a white, blotchy, grinning face at his elbow.

"I maun congratulate ye, Mr. Moore. Ye've beat us — you and the gentlemen — judges."

"'Twas a close thing, M'Adam," the other answered. "An' yo' made a gran' fight. In ma life I niver saw a finer turn than yours by the two flags yonder. I hope yo' bear no malice."

"Malice! Me? Is it likely? Na, na. 'Do onto ivery man as he does onto you — and somethin' over,' that's my motter. I owe ye mony a good turn, which I'll pay ye yet. Na, na; there's nae good fechtin' agin fate — and the judges. Weel, I wush you well o'yer victory. Aiblins 'twill be oor turn next."

Then a rush, headed by Sam'l, roughly hustled the one away and bore the other off on its shoulders in boisterous triumph.

*   *   *

In giving the Cup away, Lady Eleanour made a prettier speech than ever. Yet all the while she was haunted by a white, miserable face; and all the while she was conscious of two black moving dots in the Murk Muir Pass opposite her — solitary, desolate, a contrast to the huzzaing crowd around.

*   *   *

That is how the champion challenge Dale Cup, the world-known Shepherds' Trophy, came to wander no more; won outright by the last of the Gray Dogs of Kenmuir — Owd Bob.

Why he was the last of the Gray Dogs is now to be told.

5. A RUNAWAY

from *The Man on the Box* [Chapt. XIII]
by Harold MacGrath, 1904

*One of the nicest things in Victorian novels which is left
out of contemporary novels is horses. Unless, that is,
your taste runs to Westerns. In the following chapter
from* The Man on the Box *Harold MacGrath gives the
horse-lover his favorite animal from a head full of mischief to carefully oiled hooves. And all the action of
both men and horses dear to armchair adventurers of
any generation packs itself into a runaway which
thunders over five miles of dusty roads that wind
through the Maryland countryside.*

*MacGrath's later success as a writer of detective
stories is foreshadowed in this romance of a Russian
spy, a man who plans to commit treason, and an ex-
soldier playing groom who is the hero both of the
runaway and of the whole story. It is for love, of course,
that Lieutenant Robert Warburton, late of the United
States Army, masquerades as a groom in the household
of George Annesley, Colonel (Ret.), USA. The beautiful*

Miss Betty Annesley is the cause of Robert's troubles — the runaway, the masquerading, and all the rest of it. The "Nancy" referred to is Robert's sister and a friend of Betty's since their schooldays, when Robert was on duty with the blue-coated cavalry in Arizona.

Robert has recently resigned his commission, and has returned, after a trip to Europe, to civilized Washington. His head is apparently still full of the Wild West. The night he arrives in town he conceives the novel idea of giving his sister Nancy and his sister-in-law a thrill by disguising himself as his brother's groom, calling for the ladies in the family carriage as they leave a fashionable ball, and giving them a wild ride around the genteel "circles" in the nation's capital before hauling up his powerful team of horses and explaining the joke. The mounted police who thunder after the carriage do not see the joke. Neither do the two ladies in the carriage, who turn out to be not Robert's relatives but Miss Betty Annesley and her companion. Robert, who has seen Miss Annesley during his voyage home from Europe and been instantly smitten, is horrified, but consoles himself with the thought that Betty cannot recognize him, since they were not introduced during the ocean crossing and since he has sacrificed his beard in order to play the role of groom. Betty, of course, does recognize him; is intrigued; and when she is required to appear in court the next day drops charges against him and offers him a position as groom in her father's household. Thereafter she plays a game with him, even allowing the family cook, Pierre, to chide him, in order to see how long he will keep up his masquerade.

The villain of this chapter, Pirate, is a handsome horse with a mind so much his own that no one has dared ride him for a year or more until Mr. Robert has subdued him, temporarily, a few days before "A Runaway" begins. It was by conquering Pirate that Robert won his place as groom in the Annesley household.

The Man on the Box, *written in 1904, was popular both as a novel and as a play. It ran for 123 nights at the Madison Square Theater in New York.*

Four days passed. I might have used the word "sped," only that verb could not be truthfully applied. Never before in the history of time (so our jehu thought) did four days cast their shadows more slowly across the dial of the hours. From noon till night there was a madding nothing to do but polish bits and buckles and stirrups and ornamental silver. He would have been totally miserable but for the morning rides. These were worth while; for he was riding Pirate, and there was always that expectation of the unexpected. But Pirate behaved himself puzzlingly well. Fortunately for the jehu, these rides were always into the north country. He was continually possessed with fear lest she would make him drive through the shopping district. If he met Nancy, it would be, in the parlance of the day, all off. Nancy would have recognized him in a beard like a Cossack's; and here he was with the boy's face — the face she never would forget.

He was desperately in love. I do not know what desperately in love is, my own love's course running smoothly enough; but I can testify that it was making Mr. Robert thin and appetiteless. Every morning the impulse came to him to tell her all; but every morning his courage oozed like Bob Acres', and his lips became dumb. I dare say that if she had questioned him he would have told her all; but for some reason she had ceased to inquire into his past. Possibly her young mind was occupied with pleasanter things.

He became an accomplished butler, and served so well in rehearsals that Pierre could only grumble. One afternoon she superintended the comedy. She found a thousand faults with him, so many, in fact, that Pierre did not understand what it meant, and became possessed with the vague idea that she was hitting him over the groom's shoulder. He did not like it; and later, when they were alone, Warburton was distinctly impressed with Pierre's displeasure.

"You can not please *her*, and you can not please *me*. Bah! Zat ees vat comes uf teaching a groom table manners instead uf stable manners. And you vill smell uf horse! I do *not* understand Miss Annesley; no!"

And there were other humiliations, petty ones. She chid him on having the stirrup too long or too short; the curb chain was rusting; this piece of ornamental silver did not shine like that one; Jane's fetlocks were too long; Pirate's hoofs weren't thoroughly oiled. With dogged patience he tried to remedy all these faults. It was only when they had had a romping run down the road that this spirit fell away from her, and she talked pleasantly.

Twice he ran into Karloff; but that shrewd student of human nature did not consider my hero worth studying; a grave mistake on his part, as he was presently to learn. He was a handsome man, and the only thing he noticed about the groom was his handsome face. He considered it a crime for a servant to be endowed with personal attractions. A servant in the eyes of a Russian noble excites less interest than a breedless dog. Mr. Robert made no complaint; he was very well satisfied to have the count ignore him entirely. Once he met the count in the Turkish room, where, in the capacity of butler, he served liqueur and cigars. There was a certain grim humor in lighting his rival's cigar for him. This service was a test of his ability to pass through a room without knocking over taborets and chairs. Another time they met, when Betty and the two of them took a long ride. Karloff *did* notice how well the groom rode his mettlesome mount, being himself a soldier and a daring horseman. Warburton had some trouble. Pirate did not take to the idea of breathing Jane and Dick's dust; he wanted to lead these second-raters. Mr. James' arms ached that afternoon from the effort he had put forth to restrain Pirate and keep him in his proper place, five yards to the rear.

Nothing happened Sunday; the day went by uneventfully. He escaped the ordeal of driving her to the Chevy Chase Club, William being up that afternoon.

The Monday came, and with it Betty's curious determination to ride Pirate.

"You wish to ride Pirate, Miss?" exclaimed James, his horror of the idea openly manifest.

"Saddle him for me," — peremptorily. "I desire to ride him. I find Jane isn't exciting enough."

"Pardon me, Miss Annesley," he said, "but I had rather you would not make the attempt."

"You had rather I would not make the attempt?" — slowly repeating the words, making a knife of each one of them, tipped with the poison of her contempt. "I do not believe I quite understand you."

He bravely met the angry flash of her eyes. There were times when the color of these eyes did not resemble sapphires; rather disks of gunmetal, caused by a sudden dilation of the pupils.

"Yes, Miss, I had rather you would not."

"James, you forget yourself. Saddle Pirate, and take Jane back to the stables. Besides, Jane has a bit of a cold." She slapped her boot with her riding-crop and indolently studied the scurrying clouds overhead; for the day was windy.

Soberly Warburton obeyed. He was hurt and angry, and he knew not what besides. Heavens, if anything should happen to her! His hopes rose a bit. Pirate had shown no temper so far that morning. He docilely permitted his master to put on the side-saddle. But as he came out into the air again, he threw forward his ears, stretched out his long black neck, took in a great breath, and whinnied a hoarse challenge to the elements. William had already saddled Dick, who looked askance at his black rival's small compact heels.

"I am afraid of him," said Warburton, as he returned. "He will run away with you. I did not wholly subjugate him the other day. He pulls till my arms ache."

Miss Annesley shrugged and patted Pirate on the nose and offered him a lump of sugar. The thirst for freedom and a wild run down the wind lurked in Pirate's far-off gazing eyes, and he ignored the sign of conciliation which his mistress made him.

"I am not afraid of him. Besides, Dick can outrun and outjump him."

This did not reassure Warburton, nor did he know what this comparison meant, being an ordinary mortal.

"With all due respect to you, Miss Annesley, I am sorry that you are determined to ride him. He is most emphatically not a lady's horse, and you have never ridden him. Your skirts will irritate him, and if he sees your crop, he'll bolt."

She did not reply, but merely signified her desire to mount. No sooner was she up, however, than she secretly regretted her caprice; but not for a hundred worlds would she have permitted this groom to know. But Pirate, with that rare instinct of the horse, knew that his mistress was not sure of him. He showed the whites of his eyes and began pawing the gravel. The girl glanced covertly at her groom and found no color in his cheeks. Two small muscular lumps appeared at the corners of her jaws. She would ride Pirate, and nothing should stop her; nothing, nothing. Womanlike, knowing herself to be in the wrong, she was furious.

And Pirate surprised them both. During the first mile he behaved himself in the most gentlemanly fashion; and if he shied once or twice, waltzed a little, it was only because he was full of life and spirit. They trotted, they cantered, ran and walked. Warburton, hitherto holding himself in readiness for whatever might happen, relaxed the tension of his muscles, and his shoulders sank relievedly. Perhaps, after all, his alarm had been needless. The trouble with Pirate might be the infrequency with which he had been saddled and ridden. But he knew that the girl would not soon forget his interference. There would be more humiliations, more bitter pills for him to swallow. It pleased him, however, to note the ease with which Dick kept pace with Pirate.

As for the most beautiful person in all the great world, I am afraid that she was beginning to feel self-important. Now that her confidence was fully restored, she never once spoke to, or looked at, her groom. Occasionally from the corner of her eye she could see the white patch on Dick's nose.

"James," she said maliciously and suddenly, "go back five yards. I wish to ride alone."

Warburton, his face burning, fell back. And thus she made her first mistake. The second and final mistake came immediately after. She touched Pirate with her heel, and he broke from a trot into a lively gallop. Dick, without a touch of the boot, kept his distance to a foot.

Pirate, no longer seeing Dick at his side, concluded that he had left his rival behind; and the suppressed mischief in his black head began to find an outlet. Steadily he began to arch his neck; steadily but surely he drew down on the reins. The girl felt the effort and tried to frustrate it. In backing her pull with her right hand, the end of her crop flashed down the side of Pirate's head — the finishing touch. There was a wild leap, a blur of dust, and Mr. Pirate, well named after his freebooting sires, his head down where he wanted it, his feet rolling like a snare-drum, Mr. Pirate ran away, headed for heaven only knew where.

For a brief moment Warburton lost his nerve; he was struck wtih horror. If she could not hold her seat, she would be killed or dreadfully hurt, and perhaps disfigured. It seemed rather strange, as he recalled it, that Dick, instead of himself, should have taken the initiative. The noble sorrel, formerly a cavalry horse, shot forward magnificently. Doubtless his horsesense took in the situation, or else he did not like the thought of yonder proud, supercilious show-horse beating him in a running race. So, a very fast mile was put to the rear.

The girl, appreciating her peril, did as all good horsewomen would have done: locked her knees on the horn and held on. The rush of wind tore the pins from her hair which, like a golden plume, stretched out behind her. (Have you ever read anything like this before? I dare say. But to Warburton and the girl, it never occurred that other persons had gone through like episodes. It was real, and actual, and single, and tragic to them.)

The distance between the two horses began slowly to lessen, and Warburton understood, in a nebulous way, what the girl had meant when she said that Dick could outrun Pirate. If Pirate kept to the road, Dick would bring him down; but if Pirate took it into his head to vault a fence! Warburton shuddered. Faster, faster, over this roll of earth, clattering across this bridge, around this curve and that angle. Once the sight of a team drawing a huge grain-wagon sent a shiver to Warburton's heart. But they thundered past with a foot to spare. The old negro on the seat stared after them, his ebony face drawn with wonder and the whites of his eyes showing.

Foot by foot, yard by yard, the space lessened, till Dick's nose was within three feet of Pirate's flowing tail. Warburton fairly lifted Dick along with his knees. I only wish I could describe the race as my jehu told it to me. The description held me by the throat. I could see the flashing by of trees and houses and fields; the scampering of piccaninnies across the road; the horses from the meadows dashing up to fences and whinnying; the fine stone and dust which Pirate's rattling heels threw into my jehu's face and eyes; the old pain throbbing anew in his leg. And when he finally drew alongside the black brute and saw the white, set face of the girl he loved, I can imagine no greater moment but one in his life. There was no fear on her face, but there was appeal in her eyes as she half turned her head. He leaned across the intervening space and slid his arm around her waist. The two horses came together and twisted his leg cruelly. His jaws snapped.

"Let the stirrup go!" he cried. "Let go quick!" She

heard him. "Your knee from the horn! I can't keep them together any longer. Now!"

Brave and plucky and cool she was. She obeyed him instantly. There was a mighty heave, a terrible straining of the back and the knees, and Pirate was freed of his precious burden. The hardest part of it came now. Dick could not be made to slow down abruptly. He wanted to keep right on after his rival. So, between holding the girl with his right arm and pulling the horse with his left, Warburton saw that he could keep up this terrible effort but a very short time. Her arms were convulsively wound around his neck, and this added to the strain. Not a word did she say; her eyes were closed, as if she expected any moment to be dashed to the earth.

But Dick was only a mortal horse. The fierce run and the double burden began to tell, and shortly his head came up. Warburton stopped him. The girl slid to the ground, and in a moment he was at her side. And just in time. The reaction was too much for her. Dazedly she brushed her hair from her eyes, stared wildly at Warburton, and fainted. He did not catch her with that graceful precision which on the stage is so familiar to us. No. He was lucky to snatch one of her arms, thus preventing her head from striking the road. He dragged her to the side of the highway and rested her head on his shaking knees. Things grew dark for a time. To tell the truth, he himself was very close to that feminine weakness which the old fellows, in their rough and ready plays, used to call "vapours". But he forced his heart to steady itself.

And what do you suppose the rascal did — with nobody but Dick to watch him? Why, he did what any healthy young man in love would have done: pressed his lips to the girl's hair, his eyes filling and half a sob in his parched throat. He dolefully pictured himself a modern Antiochus, dying of love and never confessing it. Then he kissed her hair again; only her hair, for somehow he felt that her lips and cheeks were as yet inviolable to his touch. I should have liked to see the picture they made: the panting horse a dozen rods away, looking at them inquiringly; the girl in her dust-covered habit; her hair spreading out like seaweed on a wave, her white face, her figure showing its graceful lines; my jehu, his hair matted to his brow, the streaks of dust and perspiration on his face, the fear and love and longing in his dark eyes. I recollect a picture called *Love and Honor,* or something like that. It never appealed to me. It lacked action. It simply represented a fellow urging a girl to elope with him. Both of them were immaculately dressed. But here, on this old highway leading into Maryland, was something real. A battle had been fought and won.

Fainting is but transitory; by and by she opened her eyes, and stared vaguely into the face above her. I do not know what she saw there; whatever it was it caused her to struggle to her feet. There was color enough in her cheeks now; and there was a question, too, in her eyes. Of Warburton it asked, "What did you do when I lay there unconscious?" I'm afraid there was color in his face, too. Her gaze immediately roved up the road. There was no Pirate, only a haze of dust. Doubtless he was still going it, delighted over the trouble he had managed to bring about. Warburton knelt at the girl's side and brushed the dust from her skirt. She eyed him curiously. I shan't say that she smiled; I don't know, for I wasn't there.

Meanwhile she made several futile attempts to put up her hair, and as a finality she braided it and let it hang down her back. Suddenly and unaccountably she grew angry — angry at herself, at James, at the rascally horse that had brought her to this pass. Warburton saw something of this emotion in her eyes, and to avoid the storm he walked over to Dick, picked up the reins, and led him back.

"If you will mount Dick, Miss," he said, "I will lead him home. It's about five miles, I should say."

The futility and absurdity of her anger aroused her sense of the ridiculous; and a smile, warm and merry, flashed over her stained face. It surprised her groom.

"Thank you, James. You were right. I ought not to have ridden Pirate. I am punished for my conceit. Five miles? It will be a long walk."

"I shan't mind it in the least," replied James, inordinately happy; and he helped her to the saddle and adjusted the left stirrup.

So the journey home began. Strangely enough, neither seemed to care particularly what had or might become of Pirate. He disappeared, mentally and physically. One thing dampened the journey for Warburton. His "game leg" ached cruelly, and after the second mile (which was traversed without speech from either of them), he fell into a slight limp. From her seat above and behind him, she saw this limp.

"You have hurt yourself?" she asked gently.

"Not to-day, Miss," — briefly.

"When he ran away with you?"

"No. It's an old trouble."

"While you were a soldier?"

"Yes."

"How?"

He turned in surprise. All these questions were rather unusual. Nevertheless he answered her, and truthfully.

"I was shot in the leg by a drunken Indian."

"While on duty?"

"Yes." Unconsciously he was forgetting to add "Miss", which was the patent of his servility. And I do not think that just then she noticed this subtraction from the respect due her.

It was eleven o'clock when they arrived at the gates. She dismounted alone. Warburton was visibly done up.

"Any orders for this afternoon, Miss?"

"I shall want the victoria at three. I have some shopping to do and a call to make. Send William after Pirate. I am very grateful for what you have done."

He made no reply, for he saw her father coming down the steps.

"Betty," said the colonel, pale and worried, "have you been riding Pirate? Where is he, and what in the world has happened?" — noting the dust on her habit and her tangled hair.

She explained: she told the story rather coolly, Warburton thought, but she left out no detail.

"You have James to thank for my safety, father. He was very calm and clear-headed."

Calm and clear-headed! thought Warburton.

The girl then entered the house, humming. Most women would have got out the lavender salts and lain down the rest of the day, considering the routine of a fashionable dinner, which was the chief duty of the evening.

"I am grateful to you, James. My daughter is directly in your care when she rides, and I give you full authority. Never permit her to mount any horse but her own. She is all I have; and if anything should happen to her —"

"Yes, sir; I understand."

The colonel followed his daughter; and Warburton led Dick to the stables, gave his orders to William, and flung himself down on his cot. He was dead tired. And the hour he had dreaded was come! He was to drive her through the shopping district. Well, so be it. If any one exposed him, very good. This groom business was decidedly like work. And there was that confounded dinner-party, and he would have to limp around a table and carry soup plates! And as likely as not he would run into the very last person he expected to see.

Which he did.

6. THE ANNEXATION OF CUBY

from *Mrs. Wiggs of the Cabbage Patch* [Chapt. IV]
by Alice Caldwell (Hegan) Rice, 1901

If adventure tales such as The Man on the Box
*featured fine show horses and hunters, one of the
sorriest pieces of horseflesh to come alive in a book
since the days of Quixote's Rocinante was "Cuby,"
whose "annexation" by the indomitable Wiggs family
is one of the great charms of* Mrs. Wiggs of the
Cabbage Patch.

*Alice Caldwell (Hegan) Rice's little sugarplum of a
story depended heavily for its appeal, in 1901, on the
prevailing taste for stories of the "deserving poor" and
their wealthy benefactors; but there are moments
throughout the book when real people live real
minutes and hours and days. These moments lift* Mrs.
Wiggs *far above the level of most books of its type.
They also remind one of how very many people, even
in an America which was building its western empire,
lived from one thin dime to the next before modern
technology had worked its miraculous revolution in
agriculture and basic industries.*

"They well deserve to have,
That know the strongest and surest way to get."

Almost a year rolled over the Cabbage Patch, and it was nearing Christmas again. The void left in Mrs. Wiggs's heart by Jim's death could never be filled, but time was beginning to soften her grief, and the necessity for steady employment kept her from brooding over her trouble.

It was still needful to maintain the strictest economy, for half the money which had been given them was in Miss Olcott's keeping as a safeguard against another rainy day. Mrs. Wiggs had got as much washing as she could do; Asia helped about the house, and Billy did odd jobs wherever he could find them.

The direct road to fortune, however, according to Billy's ideas, could best be traveled in a kindling-wagon, and, while he was the proud possessor of a dilapidated wagon, sole relic of the late Mr. Wiggs, he had nothing to hitch to it. Scarcely a week passed that he did not agitate the question, and, as Mrs. Wiggs often said, "When Billy Wiggs done set his head to a thing, he's as good as got it!"

So she was not surprised when he rushed breathlessly into the kitchen one evening, about supper-time, and exclaimed in excited tones: "Ma, I've got a horse! he was havin' a fit on the commons an' they was goin' to shoot him, an' I ast the man to give him to me!"

"My land, Billy! What do you want with a fit-horse?" asked his mother.

"Cause I knowed you could cure him. The man said if I took him I'd have to pay for cartin' away his carcass, but I said, "All right, I'll take him, anyway.' Come on, ma, an' see him!" and Billy hurried back to his new possession.

Mrs. Wiggs pinned a shawl over her head and ran across the commons. A group of men stood around the writhing animal, but the late owner had departed.

"He's 'most gone," said one of the men, as she came up. "I tole Billy you'd beat him for takin' that ole nag offen the man's han's."

"Well, I won't," said Mrs. Wiggs, stoutly. "Billy Wiggs's got more sense than most men I know. That hoss's carcass is worth somethin'; I 'spect he'd bring 'bout two dollars dead, an' mebbe more livin'. Anyway, I'm goin' to save him if there's any save to him!"

She stood with her arms on her hips, and critically surveyed her patient. "I'll tell you what's the matter with him," was her final diagnosis; "his lights is riz. Billy, I'm goin' home for some medicine; you set on his head so's he can't git up, an' ma'll be right back in a minute."

The crowd which had collected to see the horse shot began to disperse, for it was supper-time, and there was nothing to see now but the poor suffering animal, with Billy Wiggs patiently sitting on its head.

When Mrs. Wiggs returned she carried a bottle, and what appeared to be a large marble. "This here is a calomel pill," she explained. "I jes' rolled the calomel in with some soft, light bread. Now, you prop his jaw open with a little stick, an' I'll shove it in, an' then hole his head back, while I pour down some water an' turkentine outen this bottle."

It was with great difficulty that this was accomplished, for the old horse had evidently seen a vision of the happy hunting-ground, and was loath to return to the sordid earth. His limbs were already stiffening in death, and the whites of his eyes only were visible. Mrs. Wiggs noted these discouraging symptoms, and saw that violent measures were necessary.

"Gether some sticks an' build a fire quick as you kin. I've got to run over home. Build it right up clost to him, Billy; we've got to git him het up."

She rushed into the kitchen, and, taking several cakes of tallow from the shelf, threw them into a tin bucket. Then she hesitated for a moment. The kettle of soup was steaming away on the stove ready for supper. Mrs. Wiggs did not believe in sacrificing the present need to the future comfort. She threw in a liberal portion of pepper, and, seizing the kettle in one hand and the bucket of tallow in the other, staggered back to the bonfire.

"Now, Billy," she commanded, "put this bucket of tallow down there in the hottest part of the fire. Look out; don't tip it — there! Now, you come here an' help me pour this soup into the bottle. I'm goin' to git that ole hoss so het up he'll think he's havin' a sunstroke! Seems sorter bad to keep on pestering him when he's so near gone, but this here soup'll feel good when it once gits inside him."

When the kettle was empty, the soup was impartially distributed over Mrs. Wiggs and the patient, but a goodly amount had "got inside," and already the horse was losing his rigidity.

Only once did Billy pause in his work, and that was to ask:

"Ma, what do you think I'd better name him?"

Giving names was one of Mrs. Wiggs' chief accomplishments, and usually required much thoughtful consideration; but in this case if there was to be a christening it must be at once.

"I'd like a jography name," suggested Billy, feeling that nothing was too good to bestow upon his treasure.

Mrs. Wiggs stood with the soup dripping from her hands, and earnestly contemplated the horse. Babies, pigs, goats, and puppies had drawn largely on her supply of late, and geography names especially were scarce. Suddenly a thought struck her.

"I'll tell you what, Billy! We'll call him Cuby! It's a town I heard 'em talkin' 'bout at the grocery."

By this time the tallow was melted, and Mrs. Wiggs carried it over by the horse, and put each of his hoofs into the hot liquid, while Billy rubbed the legs with all the strength of his young arms.

"That's right," she said; "now you run home an' git that piece of carpet by my bed, an' we'll kiver him up. I am goin' to git them fence rails over yonder to keep the fire goin'."

Through the long night they worked with their

patient, and when the first glow of morning appeared in the east, a triumphant procession wended its way across the Cabbage Patch. First came an old woman, bearing sundry pails, kettles, and bottles; next came a very sleepy little boy, leading a trembling old horse, with soup all over its head, tallow on its feet, and a strip of rag-carpet tied about its middle.

And thus Cuba, like his geographical namesake, emerged from the violent ordeal of reconstruction with a mangled constitution, internal dissension, a decided preponderance of foreign element, but a firm and abiding trust in the new power with which his fortunes had been irrevocably cast.

7. THE DUEL

from *When Knighthood Was in Flower* [Chapt. I]
by Charles Major, 1898

*When romancers of grandfather's day found themselves
running out of good adventure stories of their own
times, they had only to turn to the Middle Ages and
the Renaissance. Robber barons of their own business
world might not be recognized as suitable protagonists
for adventure stories – might, indeed, not even be
recognized as robber barons – but the romancers and
their readers knew just what to expect of the genuine
fifteenth century article. One of the things to expect
was a duel, the gorier the better. One of the goriest is
that with which Charles Major introduces the hero of his
very popular* When Knighthood Was in Flower, *re-
printed twenty-two times within a year after its
publication in September, 1898.*

*The story purports to be "the love story of Charles
Brandon and Mary Tudor, the king's sister, and
happening in the reign of his august majesty, King
Henry VIII." If history insists that Charles Brandon*

was created Duke of Suffolk before he met Mary Tudor, and in other ways tends to deflate romance, who would not prefer the version in the novel?

The story is told by a friend of Charles Brandon, Sir Edwin Caskoden, King Henry's Master of the Dance (in the Charles Major version of history).

It sometimes happens, Sir Edwin says, that when a woman will she won't, and when she won't she will; but usually in the end the adage holds good. That sentence may not be luminous with meaning, but I will give you an illustration.

I think it was in the spring of 1509, at any rate soon after the death of the "Modern Solomon," as Queen Catherine called her old father-in-law, the late King Henry VII, that his august majesty Henry VIII, "The Vndubitate Flower and very Heire of both the sayd Linages," came to the throne of England, and tendered me the honorable position of Master of the Dance at his sumptuous court.

As to "worldly goods," as some of the new religionists call wealth, I was very comfortably off; having inherited from my father, one of the counselors of Henry VII, a very competent fortune indeed. How my worthy father contrived to save from the greedy hand of that rich old miser so great a fortune, I am sure I can not tell. He was the only man of my knowledge who did it; for the old king had a reach as long as the kingdom, and, upon one pretext or another, appropriated to himself everything on which he could lay his hands. My father, however, was himself pretty shrewd at money matters, having inherited along with his fortune a rare knack for keeping it. His father was a goldsmith in the time of King Edward, and enjoyed the marked favor of that puissant prince.

Being thus in a position of affluence, I cared nothing for the fact that little or no emolument went with the office; it was the honor which delighted me. Besides, I was thereby an inmate of the king's palace, and brought into intimate relations with the court, and, above all, with the finest ladies of the land — the best company a man can keep, since it ennobles his mind with better thoughts, purifies his heart with cleaner motives, and makes him gentle without detracting from his strength. It was an office any lord of the kingdom might have been proud to hold.

Now, some four or five years after my induction to said honorable office, there came to court news of a terrible duel fought down in Suffolk, out of which only one of the four combatants had come alive — two, rather, but one of them was in a condition worse than death. The first survivor was a son of Sir William Brandon, and the second was a man called Sir Adam Judson. The story went that young Brandon and his elder brother, both just home from the continental wars, had met Judson at an Ipswich inn, where there had been considerable gambling among them. Judson had won from the brothers quite a large sum of money which they had brought home; for, notwithstanding their youth, the elder being but twenty-six and the younger about twenty-four years of age, they had gained great honor and considerable profit in the wars, especially the younger, whose name was Charles.

It is a little hard to fight for money and then lose it by a single spot upon the die, but such is the fate of him who plays, and a philosopher will swallow his ill luck and take to fighting for more. The Brandons could have done this easily enough, especially Charles, who was an offhand philosopher, rather fond of a good-humored fight, had it not been that in the course of play one evening the secret of Judson's winning had been disclosed by a discovery that he cheated. The Brandons waited until they were sure, and then trouble began, which resulted in a duel on the second morning following.

This Judson was a Scotch gentleman of whom very little was known, except that he was counted the most deadly and most cruel duelist of the time. He was called the "Walking Death," and it is said took pride in the appellation. He claimed to have fought eighty-seven duels, in which he had killed seventy-five men, and it was considered certain death to meet him. I got the story of the duel afterwards from Brandon as I give it here.

John was the elder brother, and when the challenge came was entitled to fight first; a birthright out of which Charles tried in vain to talk him. The brothers told their father, Sir William Brandon, and at the appointed time father and sons repaired to the place of meeting, where they found Judson and his two seconds ready for the fight.

Sir William was still a vigorous man, with few equals in sword play, and the sons, especially the younger, were better men and more skillful than their father had ever been, yet they felt this duel meant certain death, so great was Judson's fame for skill and cruelty. Notwithstanding they were so handicapped with this feeling of impending evil, they met their duty without a tremor; for the motto of their house was, "Malo Mori Quam Fedrai."

It was a misty morning in March. Brandon has told me since, that when his elder brother took his stand, it was at once manifest that he was Judson's superior, both in strength and skill, but after a few strokes the brother's blade bent double and broke off at the hilt when it should have gone home. Thereupon, Judson, with a malignant smile of triumph, deliberately selected his opponent's heart and pierced it with his sword, giving the blade a twist as he drew it out in order to cut and mutilate the more.

In an instant Sir William's doublet was off, and he was in his dead son's tracks, ready to avenge him or die. Again the thrust which should have killed broke the sword, and the father died as the son had died.

After this, came young Charles, expecting, but, so great was his strong heart, not one whit fearing, to lie beside his dead father and brother. He knew he was the superior of both in strength and skill, and his knowledge of men and the Noble Art told him they had each been the superior of Judson; but the fellow's hand seemed to be the hand of death. An opening came through Judson's unskillful play, which gave young Brandon an opportunity for a thrust to kill, but his blade, like his father's and brother's, bent double without penetrating. Unlike the others, however, it did not break, and the thrust revealed the fact that Judson's skill as a duelist lay in a shirt of mail which it was useless to try to pierce. Aware of this, Brandon knew that victory was his, and that soon he would have avenged the murders that had gone before. He saw that his adversary was strong neither in wind nor arm, and had not the skill to penetrate his guard in a week's trying, so he determined to fight on the defensive until Judson's strength should wane, and then kill him when and how he chose.

After a time Judson began to breathe hard and his thrusts to lack force.

"Boy, I would spare you," he said; "I have killed enough of your tribe; put up your sword and call it quits."

Young Brandon replied: "Stand your ground, you coward; you will be a dead man as soon as you grow a little weaker; if you try to run I will thrust you through the neck as I would a cur. Listen how you snort. I shall soon have you; you are almost gone. You would spare me, would you? I could preach a sermon or dance a hornpipe while I am killing you. I will not break my sword against your coat of mail, but will wait until you fall from weakness and then. . . . Fight, you bloodhound!"

Judson was pale from exhaustion, and his breath

was coming in gasps as he tried to keep the merciless sword from his throat. At last, by a dexterous twist of his blade, Brandon sent Judson's sword flying thirty feet away. The fellow started to run, but turned and fell upon his knees to beg for life. Brandon's reply was a flashing circle of steel, and his sword point cut lengthwise through Judson's eyes and the bridge of his nose, leaving him sightless and hideous for life. A revenge compared to which death would have been merciful.

The duel created quite a sensation throughout the kingdom, for although little was known as to who Judson was, his fame as a duelist was as broad as the land. He had been at court upon several occasions, and, at one time, upon the king's birthday, had fought in the royal lists. So the matter came in for its share of consideration by king and courtiers, and young Brandon became a person of interest. He became still more so when some gentlemen who had served with him in the continental wars told the court of his daring and bravery, and related stories of deeds at arms worthy of the best knight in Christendom.

He had an uncle at the court, Sir Thomas Brandon, the king's Master of Horse, who thought it a good opportunity to put his nephew forward and let him take his chance at winning royal favor. The uncle broached the subject to the king, with favorable issue, and Charles Brandon, led by the hand of fate, came to London Court, where that same fate had in keeping for him events such as seldom fall to the lot of man.

8. OUR SOCIETY

from *Cranford* [Chapt. I]
by Elizabeth Gaskell, 1853

From Jane Austen to Virginia Woolf, women novelists have shown a special aptitude for discovering the drama inherent in a tea party, or other surface-placid domestic situation, which may, in fact, be the eye of a hurricane. If Victorian readers liked their authentic adventure stories to be as swashbuckling as possible, they were nevertheless quick to see that Elizabeth Gaskell's Cranford, *which looks at first glance like a still life of an English village in the early nineteenth century, has action of its own kind in plenty. The adventures in* Cranford *are teacup size; but apparently there were many Victorian realists who recognized that much of life is measured out, if not in coffee spoons, at least in saucers of the proper size for tea drinking.*

Cranford, *painted as delicately as any bit of Wedgewood queen's ware, came out in 1853 and early established itself as a favorite among Mrs. Gaskell's writings. This daughter and wife of Unitarian clergy-men has much to say in novels like* Mary Barton *and* North and South *about conditions among laborers in the mills of northern England. Her novel* Ruth *pleads for a single standard of sexual morality. Her* Life of Charlotte Bronte *is considered one of the finest of Victorian biographies. But it is* Cranford *whose appeal has been widest and most enduring.*

In the chapter given here we meet the ladies of Cranford — and Captain Brown, the one bass voice to be distinguished among the sopranos and altos when a hymn is sung in Cranford church.

In the first place, Cranford is in possession of the Amazons; all the holders of houses, above a certain rent, are women. If a married couple come to settle in the town, somehow the gentleman disappears; he is either fairly frightened to death by being the only man in Cranford evening parties, or he is accounted for by being with his regiment, his ship, or closely engaged in business all the week in the great neighbouring commercial town of Drumble, distant only twenty miles on a railroad. In short, whatever does become of the gentlemen, they are not at Cranford. What could they do if they were there? The surgeon has his round of thirty miles, and sleeps at

Cranford; but every man cannot be a surgeon. For keeping the trim gardens full of choice flowers without a weed to speck them; for frightening away little boys who look wistfully at the said flowers through the railings; for rushing out at the geese that occasionally venture into the gardens if the gates are left open; for deciding all questions of literature and politics without troubling themselves with unnecessary reasons or arguments; for obtaining clear and correct knowledge of everybody's affairs in the parish; for keeping their neat maidservants in admirable order; for kindness (somewhat dictatorial) to the poor, and real tender good offices to each other whenever they were in distress, – the ladies of Cranford are quite sufficient. "A man," as one of them observed to me once, "is so in the way in the house!" Although the ladies of Cranford know all each other's proceedings, they are exceedingly indifferent to each other's opinions. Indeed, as each has her own individuality, not to say eccentricity, pretty strongly developed, nothing is *so* easy as verbal retaliation; but, somehow, goodwill reigns among them to a considerable degree.

The Cranford ladies have only an occasional little quarrel, spirted out in a few peppery words and angry jerks of the head; just enough to prevent the even tenor of their lives from becoming too flat. Their dress is very independent of fashion; as they observe, "What does it signify how we dress here at Cranford, where everybody knows us?" And if they go from home, their reason is equally cogent, "What does it signify how we dress here, where nobody knows us?" The materials of their clothes are, in general, good and plain, and most of them are nearly as scrupulous as Miss Tyler, of cleanly memory; but I will answer for it, the last gigot, the last tight and scanty petticoat in wear in England, was seen in Cranford — and seen without a smile.

I can testify to a magnificent family red silk umbrella, under which a gentle little spinster, left alone of many brothers and sisters, used to patter to church on rainy days. Have you any red silk umbrellas in London? We had a tradition of the first that had ever been seen in Cranford; and the little boys mobbed it, and called it "a stick in petticoats." It might have been the very red silk one I have described, held by a strong father over a troop of little ones; the poor little lady — the survivor of all — could scarcely carry it.

Then there were rules and regulations for visiting and calls; and they were announced to any young people, who might be staying in the town, with all the solemnity with which the old Manx laws were read once a year on the Tinwald Mount.

"Our friends have sent to inquire how you are after your journey to-night, my dear" (fifteen miles in a gentleman's carriage); "they will give you some rest to-morrow, but the next day, I have no doubt, they will call; so be at liberty after twelve — from twelve to three are our calling-hours."

Then, after they had called —

"It is the third day; I daresay your mamma has told

you, my dear, never to let more than three days elapse between receiving a call and returning it; and also, that you are never to stay longer than a quarter of an hour."

"But am I to look at my watch? How am I to find out when a quarter of an hour has passed?"

"You must keep thinking about the time, my dear, and not allow yourself to forget it in conversation."

As everybody had this rule in their minds, whether they received or paid a call, of course no absorbing subject was ever spoken about. We kept ourselves to short sentences of small talk, and were punctual to our time.

I imagine that a few of the gentlefolks of Cranford were poor, and had some difficulty in making both ends meet; but they were like the Spartans, and concealed their smart under a smiling face. We none of us spoke of money, because that subject savoured of commerce and trade, and though some might be poor, we were all aristocratic. The Cranfordians had that kindly *esprit de corps* which made them overlook all deficiencies in success when some among them tried to conceal their poverty. When Mrs. Forrester, for instance, gave a party in her baby-house of a dwelling, and the little maiden disturbed the ladies on the sofa by a request that she might get the tea-tray out from underneath, every one took this novel proceeding as the most natural thing in the world, and talked on about household forms and ceremonies as if we all believed that our hostess had a regular servants' hall, second table, with housekeeper and steward, instead of the one little charity-school maiden, whose short ruddy arms could never have been strong enough to carry the tray up-stairs if she had not been assisted in private by her mistress, who now sat in state, pretending not to know what cakes were sent up, though she knew, and we knew, and she knew that we knew, and we knew that she knew that we knew, she had been busy all the morning making tea-bread and sponge-cakes.

There were one or two consequences arising from this general but unacknowledged poverty, and this much acknowledged gentility, which were not amiss, and which might be introduced into many circles of society to their great improvement. For instance, the inhabitants of Cranford kept early hours, and clattered home in their pattens, under the guidance of a lantern-bearer, about nine o'clock at night; and the whole town was abed and asleep by half-past ten. Moreover, it was considered "vulgar" (a tremendous word in Cranford) to give anything expensive, in the way of eatable or drinkable, at the evening entertainments. Wafer bread-and-butter and sponge-biscuits were all that the Honourable Mrs. Jamieson gave; and she was sister-in-law to the late Earl of Glenmire, although she did practise such "elegant economy."

"Elegant economy!" How naturally one falls back into the phraseology of Cranford! There, economy was always "elegant," and money-spending always "vulgar and ostentatious"; a sort of sour grapism which made us very peaceful and satisfied. I shall never forget the dismay felt when a certain Captain Brown came to live at Cranford, and openly spoke about his being poor — not in a whisper to an intimate friend, the doors and windows being previously closed, but in the public street! in a loud and military voice! alleging his poverty as a reason for not taking a particular house. The ladies of Cranford were already rather moaning over the invasion of their territories by a man and a gentleman. He was a half-pay Captain, and had obtained some situation on a neighbouring railroad, which had been vehemently petitioned against by the little town; and if, in addition to his masculine gender, and his connection with the obnoxious railroad, he was so brazen as to talk of being poor — why, then, indeed, he must be sent to Coventry. Death was as true and as common as poverty; yet people never spoke about that, loud out in the streets. It was not a word to be mentioned to ears polite. We had tacitly agreed to ignore that any with whom we associated on terms of visiting equality could ever be prevented by poverty from doing anything that they wished. If we walked to or from a party, it was because the night was *so* fine, or the air *so* refreshing, not because sedan chairs were expensive. If we wore prints, instead of summer silks, it was because we preferred a washing material; and so on, till we blinded ourselves to the vulgar fact that we were, all of us, people of very moderate means. Of course, then, we did not know what to make of a man who could speak of poverty as if it was not a disgrace. Yet, somehow, Captain Brown made himself respected in Cranford, and was called upon, in spite of all resolutions to the contrary. I was surprised to hear his opinions quoted as an authority at a visit which I paid to Cranford about a year after he had settled in the town. My own friends had been among the bitterest opponents of any proposal to visit the Captain and his daughters only twelve months before; and now he was even admitted in the tabooed hours before twelve. True, it was to discover the cause of a smoking chimney, before the fire was lighted; but still Captain Brown walked upstairs, nothing daunted, spoke in a voice too large for the room, and joked quite in the way of a tame man about the house. He had been blind to all the small slights, and omissions of trivial ceremonies, with which he had been received. He had been friendly, though the Cranford ladies had been cool; he had answered small sarcastic compliments in good faith; and with his manly frankness had overpowered all the shrinking which met him as a man who was not ashamed to be poor. And, at last, his excellent masculine common sense, and his facility in devising expedients to overcome domestic dilemmas, had gained him an extraordinary place as authority among the Cranford ladies. He himself went on his course, as unaware of his popularity as he had been of the reverse; and I am sure he was startled one day when he found his advice so highly esteemed as to make some counsel which he had given in jest to be taken in sober, serious earnest.

It was on this subject: An old lady had an Alderney

cow, which she looked upon as a daughter. You could not pay the short quarter-of-an-hour call without being told of the wonderful milk or wonderful intelligence of this animal. The whole town knew and kindly regarded Miss Betsy Barker's Alderney; therefore great was the sympathy and regret when, in an unguarded moment, the poor cow tumbled into a lime pit. She moaned so loudly that she was soon heard and rescued; but meanwhile the poor beast had lost most of her hair, and came out looked naked, cold, and miserable, in a bare skin. Everybody pitied the animal, though a few could not restrain their smiles at her droll appearance. Miss Betsy Barker absolutely cried with sorrow and dismay; and it was said she thought of trying a bath of oil. This remedy, perhaps, was recommended by some one of the number whose advice she asked; but the proposal, if ever it was made, was knocked on the head by Captain Brown's decided, "Get her a flannel waistcoat and flannel drawers, ma'am, if you wish to keep her alive. But my advice is, kill the poor creature at once."

Miss Betsy Barker dried her eyes, and thanked the Captain heartily; she set to work, and by and by all the town turned out to see the Alderney meekly going to her pasture, clad in dark gray flannel. I have watched her myself many a time. Do you ever see cows dressed in gray flannel in London?

Captain Brown had taken a small house on the out-skirts of the town, where he lived with his two daughters. He must have been upwards of sixty at the

time of the first visit I paid to Cranford after I had
left it as a residence. But he had a wiry, well-trained,
elastic figure, a stiff military throw-back of his head,
and a springing step, which made him appear much
younger than he was. His eldest daughter looked
almost as old as himself, and betrayed the fact that his
real was more than his apparent age. Miss Brown must
have been forty; she had a sickly, pained, careworn
expression on her face, and looked as if the gaiety of
youth had long faded out of sight. Even when young
she must have been plain and hard-featured. Miss
Jessie Brown was ten years younger than her sister,
and twenty shades prettier. Her face was round and
dimpled. Miss Jenkyns once said, in a passion against
Captain Brown (the cause of which I will tell you
presently), "that she thought it was time for Miss
Jessie to leave off her dimples, and not always be trying to look like a child." It was true there was something childlike in her face; and there will be, I think,
till she dies, though she should live to be a hundred.
Her eyes were large blue wondering eyes, looking
straight at you; her nose was unformed and snub, and
her lips were red and dewy; she wore her hair, too, in
little rows of curls, which heightened this appearance.
I do not know whether she was pretty or not; but I
liked her face, and so did everybody, and I do not
think she could help her dimples. She had something
of her father's jauntiness of gait and manner; and any
female observer might detect a slight difference in the
attire of the two sisters — that of Miss Jessie being

about two pounds per annum more expensive than Miss Brown's. Two pounds was a large sum in Captain Brown's annual disbursements.

Such was the impression made upon me by the Brown family when I first saw them all together in Cranford Church. The Captain I had met before — on the occasion of the smoky chimney, which he had cured by some simple alteration of the flue. In church, he held his double eye-glass to his eyes during the Morning Hymn, and then lifted up his head erect and sang out loud and joyfully. He made the responses louder than the clerk — an old man with a piping feeble voice, who, I think, felt aggrieved at the Captain's sonorous bass, and quavered higher and higher in consequence.

On coming out of the church, the brisk Captain paid the most gallant attention to his two daughters. He nodded and smiled to his acquaintances; but he shook hands with none until he had helped Miss Brown to unfurl her umbrella, had relieved her of her prayer-book, and had waited patiently till she, with trembling nervous hands, had taken up her gown to walk through the wet roads.

I wondered what the Cranford ladies did with Captain Brown at their parties. We had often rejoiced, in former days, that there was no gentleman to be attended to, and to find conversation for, at the card-parties. We had congratulated ourselves upon the snugness of the evenings; and, in our love for gentility and distaste of mankind, we had almost persuaded ourselves that to be a man was to be "vulgar"; so that when I found my friend and hostess, Miss Jenkyns, was going to have a party in my honour, and that Captain and the Miss Browns were invited, I wondered much what would be the course of the evening. Card-tables, with green-baize tops, were set out by daylight, just as usual; it was the third week in November, so the evenings closed in about four. Candles and clean packs of cards were arranged on each table. The fire was made up; the neat maidservant had received her last directions; and there we stood, dressed in our best, each with a candle-lighter in our hands, ready to dart at the candles as soon as the first knock came. Parties in Cranford were solemn festivities, making the ladies feel gravely elated as they sat together in their best dresses. As soon as three had arrived, we sat down to "Preference," I being the unlucky fourth. The next four comers were put down immediately to another table; and presently the tea-trays, which I had seen set out in the storeroom as I passed in the morning, were placed each on the middle of a card-table. The china was delicate egg-shell; the old-fashioned silver glittered with polishing; but the eatables were of the slightest description. While the trays were yet on the tables, Captain and the Miss Browns came in; and I could see that, somehow or other, the Captain was a favourite with all the ladies present. Ruffled brows were smoothed, sharp voices lowered at his approach. Miss Brown looked ill, and depressed almost to gloom. Miss Jessie smiled as usual, and seemed nearly as popular as her father. He immediately and quietly assumed the man's place in the room; attended to every one's wants, lessened the pretty maidservant's labour by waiting on empty cups and bread-and-butterless ladies; and yet did it all in so easy and dignified a manner, and so much as if it were a matter of course for the strong to attend to the weak, that he was a true man throughout. He played for threepenny points with as grave an interest as if they had been pounds; and yet, in all his attention to strangers, he had an eye on his suffering daughter — for suffering I was sure she was, though to many eyes she might only appear to be irritable. Miss Jessie could not play cards, but she talked to the sitters-out, who, before her coming, had been rather inclined to be cross. She sang, too, to an old cracked piano, which I think had been a spinnet in its youth. Miss Jessie sang "Jock o' Hazeldean" a little out of tune; but we were none of us musical, though Miss Jenkyns beat time, out of time, by way of appearing to be so.

It was very good of Miss Jenkyns to do this; for I had seen that, a little before, she had been a good deal annoyed by Miss Jessie Brown's unguarded admission (*à propos* of Shetland wool) that she had an uncle, her mother's brother, who was a shopkeeper in Edinburgh. Miss Jenkyns tried to drown this confession by a terrible cough — for the Honourable Mrs. Jamieson was sitting at the card-table nearest Miss Jessie, and what would she say or think if she found out she was in the same room with a shopkeeper's niece! But Miss

Jessie Brown (who had no tact, as we all agreed the next morning) *would* repeat the information, and assure Miss Pole she could easily get her the identical Shetland wool required, "through my uncle, who has the best assortment of Shetland goods of any one in Edinbro'." It was to take the taste of this out of our mouths, and the sound of this out of our ears, that Miss Jenkyns proposed music; so I say again, it was very good of her to beat time to the song.

When the trays reappeared with biscuits and wine, punctually at a quarter of nine, there was conversation, comparing of cards, and talking over tricks; but by and by Captain Brown sported a bit of literature.

"Have you seen any numbers of *The Pickwick Papers?*" said he. (They were then publishing in parts.) "Capital thing!"

Now Miss Jenkyns was daughter of a deceased rector of Cranford; and, on the strength of a number of manuscript sermons, and a pretty good library of divinity, considered herself literary, and looked upon any conversation about books as a challenge to her. So she answered and said, "Yes, she had seen them; indeed, she might say she had read them."

"And what do you think of them?" exclaimed Captain Brown. "Aren't they famously good?"

So urged, Miss Jenkyns could not but speak.

"I must say, I don't think they are by any means equal to Dr. Johnson. Still, perhaps, the author is young. Let him persevere, and who knows what he may become if he will take the great Doctor for his model." This was evidently too much for Captain Brown to take placidly; and I saw the words on the tip of his tongue before Miss Jenkyns had finished her sentence.

"It is quite a different sort of thing, my dear madam," he began.

"I am quite aware of that," returned she. "And I make allowances, Captain Brown."

"Just allow me to read you a scene out of this month's number," pleaded he. "I had it only this morning, and I don't think the company can have read it yet."

"As you please," said she, settling herself with an air of resignation. He read the account of the "swarry" which Sam Weller gave at Bath. Some of us laughed heartily. I did not dare, because I was staying in the house. Miss Jenkyns sat in patient gravity. When it was ended, she turned to me, and said, with mild dignity –

"Fetch me *Rasselas,* my dear, out of the book-room."

When I brought it to her she turned to Captain Brown –

"Now allow *me* to read you a scene, and then the present company can judge between your favourite, Mr. Boz, and Dr. Johnson."

She read one of the conversations between Rasselas and Imlac, in a high-pitched majestic voice; and when she had ended she said, "I imagine I am now justified in my preference of Dr. Johnson as a writer of fiction." The Captain screwed his lips up, and drummed on the table, but he did not speak. She thought she would give a finishing blow or two.

"I consider it vulgar, and below the dignity of literature, to publish in numbers."

"How was *The Rambler* published, ma'am?" asked Captain Brown, in a low voice, which I think Miss Jenkyns could not have heard.

"Dr, Johnson's style is a model for young beginners. My father recommended it to me when I began to write letters — I have formed my own style upon it; I recommend it to your favourite."

"I should be very sorry for him to exchange his style for any such pompous writing," said Captain Brown.

Miss Jenkyns felt this as a personal affront, in a way of which the Captain had not dreamed. Epistolary writing she and her friends considered as her *forte*. Many a copy of many a letter have I seen written and corrected on the slate, before she "seized the half-hour just previous to post-time to assure" her friends of this or of that; and Dr. Johnson was, as she said, her model in these compositions. She drew herself up with dignity, and only replied to Captain Brown's last remark by saying, with marked emphasis on every syllable, "I prefer Dr. Johnson to Mr. Boz."

It is said — I won't vouch for the fact — that Captain Brown was heard to say, *sotto voce*, "D — n Dr. Johnson!" If he did, he was penitent afterwards, as he showed by going to stand near Miss Jenkyns'

arm-chair, and endeavouring to beguile her into conversation on some more pleasing subject. But she was
inexorable. The next day she made the remark I have
mentioned about Miss Jessie's dimples.

9. CHAPTER TWELVE

from *T. Tembarom*
by Frances Hodgson Burnett, 1913

*Dickens, Matthew Arnold, and Henry James were only
the most famous of nineteenth century figures to
comment on what America looked like to an Englishman, or what England and the Continent looked like
to an American. Literally hundreds of less well-known
writers added their bit. Within a century after the
revolution Americans and most other people were sure
that there was such a thing as an American, and that,
whatever he was, he was different from an Englishman. This conviction provided one of the most
popular topics for thought and conversation in this
country as the United States began its second century,
and novelists made much of the "American" theme.
As late as 1913 Frances Hodgson Burnett, whose
Little Lord Fauntleroy touched on the same subject,
made the contrast between British and American life
the backbone of her mystery-romance, T. Tembarom.
A young man who has been a waif on the streets of*

New York, a newsboy and finally a reporter, discovers that he is not "T. Tembarom" but is actually "Temple Temple Barholm," heir to a great English estate. He goes to England to take over his property, and in the chapter given here encounters a phenomenon new to his universe — an English valet.

The "Strangeways" mentioned in the chapter is an English gentleman who has lost his memory and been found by T. Tembarom on the streets of New York. Tembarom has befriended the wanderer, giving him the name of "Strangeways," although others in Tembarom's boarding house call him "The Freak." Not knowing what else to do with him, Tembarom brings the sick man to England with him — conveniently, since Strangeways is later to play a key part in the story. "The Hutchinsons" are an irascible English inventor who was born in the Lancashire village connected to the Temple Barholm estate, and his daughter Ann, whom Tembarom loves. Discouraged and dissatisfied with England, Hutchinson had gone to America, where he had become discouraged and dissatisfied with the United States and fiercely loyal to England. Before leaving America, Tembarom had seen Hadman and other businessmen to assure Hutchinson of a fair chance to demonstrate the advantages that his invention would offer, not only to the world, but also to astute financiers.

The chief objection to Temple Barholm in Tembarom's mind was that it was too big for any human use. That at least was how it struck him. The entrance was too big, the stairs were too wide, the rooms too broad and too long and too high to allow of eyes accustomed to hall bedrooms adjusting their vision without discomfort. The dining-room in which the new owner took his first meal in company with Mr. Palford, and attended by the large, serious man who wore no livery and three tall footmen who did, was of a size and stateliness which made him feel homesick for Mrs. Bowse's dining-room, with its two hurried, incompetent, and often-changed waitresses and its prevailing friendly custom of pushing things across the table to save time. Meals were disposed of at Mrs. Bowse's. Everybody was due up-town or down-town, and regarded food as an unavoidable, because necessary, interference with more urgent business. At Temple Barholm one sat half the night — this was the impression made upon Tembarom — watching things being brought in and taken out of the room, carved on a huge buffet, and passed from one man to another; and when they were brought solemnly to you, if you turned them down, it seemed that the whole ceremony had to be gone through with again. All sorts of silver knives, forks, and spoons were given to one and taken away, and half a dozen sorts of glasses stood by your plate; and if you made a move to do anything for yourself, the man out of livery stopped you as though you were too big a fool to be trusted. The food was all right, but when you knew what anything was, and were inclined to welcome it as an old friend, it was given to you in some way that made you get rattled. With all the swell dishes, you had no butter-plate, and ice seemed scarce, and the dead, still way the servants moved about gave you a sort of feeling that you were at a funeral and that it wasn't decent to talk so long as the remains were in the room. The head-man and the footmen seemed to get on by signs, though Tembarom never saw them making any; and their faces never changed for a moment. Once or twice he tried a joke, addressing it to Mr. Palford, to see what would happen. But as Mr. Palford did not seem to see the humor of it, and gave him the "glassy eye," and neither the head-man nor the footmen seemed to hear it, he thought that perhaps they didn't know it was a joke; and if they didn't, and they thought anything at all, they must think he was dippy. The dinner was a deadly, though sumptuous, meal, and long drawn out, when measured by meals at Mrs. Bowse's. He did not know, as Mr. Palford did, that it was perfect, and served with a finished dexterity that was also perfection.

Mr. Palford, however, was himself relieved when it was at an end. He had sat at dinner with the late Mr. Temple Barholm in his day, and had seen him also served by the owners of impassive countenances; but he had been aware that whatsoever of secret dislike and resentment had been concealed by them, there lay behind their immovability an acceptance of the fact that he represented, even in his most objectionable humors, centuries of accustomedness to respectful service and of knowledge of his right and power to claim it. The solicitor was keenly aware of the silent comments being made upon the tweed suit and brown necktie and on the manner in which their wearer boldly chose the wrong fork or erroneously made use of a knife or spoon. Later in the evening, in the servants' hall, the comment would not be silent, and there could be no doubt of what its character would be. Housemaids and still-room maids would giggle, and kitchen-maids and boot-boys would grin and whisper in servile tribute to the witticisms of the superior servants.

After dinner the rest of the evening could at least be spent in talk about business matters. There still remained details to be enlarged upon before Palford himself returned to Lincoln's Inn and left Mr. Temple Barholm to the steward of his estate. It was not difficult to talk to him when the sole subject of conversation was of a business nature.

Before they parted for the night the mystery of the arrangements made for Strangeways had been cleared. In fact, Mr. Temple Barholm made no mystery of them. He did not seem ignorant of the fact that what he had chosen to do was unusual, but he did not appear hampered or embarrassed by the knowledge. His remarks on the subject were entirely civil and were far from actually suggesting that his singular conduct was purely his own business and none of his solicitor's; but for a moment or so Mr. Palford was privately just a trifle annoyed. The Hutchinsons had traveled from London with Strangeways in their care the day before. He would have been unhappy and disturbed if he had been obliged to travel with Mr. Palford, who was a stranger to him, and Miss Hutchinson had a soothing effect on him.

Strangeways was for the present comfortably installed as a guest of the house, Miss Hutchinson having talked to the housekeeper, Mrs. Butterworth, and to Pearson. What the future held for him Mr. Temple Barholm did not seem to feel the necessity of going into. He left him behind as a subject, and went on talking cheerfully of other things almost as if he had forgotten him.

They had their coffee in the library, and afterward sat at the writing-table and looked over documents and talked until Mr. Palford felt that he could quite decorously retire to his bedroom. He was glad to be relieved of his duties, and Tembarom was amiably resigned to parting with him.

Tembarom did not go up-stairs at once himself. He sat by the fire and smoked several pipes of tobacco and thought things over. There were a lot of things to think over, and several decisions to make, and he thought it would be a good idea to pass them in review. The quiet of the dead surrounded him. In a house the size of this the servants were probably half a mile away. They'd need trolleys to get to one, he thought, if you rang for them in a hurry. If an armed burglar made a quiet entry without your knowing it, he could get in some pretty rough work before any of the seventy-five footmen could come to lend a hand. He was not aware that there were two of them standing in waiting in the hall, their powdered heads close together, so that their whispers and chuckles could be heard. A sound of movement in the library would have brought them up standing to a decorous attitude of attention conveying to the un-initiated that they had not moved for hours.

Sometimes as he sat in the big morocco chair, T. Tembarom looked grave enough; sometimes he looked as though he was confronting problems which needed puzzling out and with which he was not making much headway; sometimes he looked as though he was thinking of little Ann Hutchinson, and not infrequently he grinned. Here he was up to the neck in it, and he was darned if he knew what he was going to do. He didn't know a soul, and nobody knew him. He didn't know a thing he ought to know, and he didn't know any one who could tell him. Even the Hutchinsons had never been inside a place like Temple Barholm, and they were going back to Manchester after a few weeks' stay at the grandmother's cottage.

Before he had left New York he had seen Hadman and some other fellows and got things started, so that there was an even chance that the invention would be put on its feet. He had worked hard and used his own power to control money in the future as a lever which had proved to be exactly what was needed.

Hadman had been spurred and a little startled when he realized the magnitude of what really could be done, and saw also that this slangy, moneyed youth was not merely an enthusiastic fool, but saw into business schemes pretty sharply and was of a most determined readiness. With this power ranging itself on the side of Hutchinson and his invention, it was good business to begin to move, if one did not want to run a chance of being left out in the cold.

Hutchinson had gone to Manchester, and there had been barely time for a brief but characteristic interview between him and Tembarom, when he rushed back to London. Tembarom felt rather excited when he remembered it, recalling what he had felt in confronting the struggles against emotion in the blunt-featured, red face, the breaks in the rough voice, the charging up and down the room like a curiously elated bull in a china shop, and the big effort to restrain relief and gratitude the degree of which might seem to under-value the merits of the invention itself.

Once or twice when he looked serious, Tembarom was thinking this over, and also once or twice when he grinned. Relief and gratitude notwithstanding, Hutchinson had kept him in his place, and had not made unbounded efforts to conceal his sense of the incongruity of his position as the controller of fortunes and the lord of Temple Barholm, which was still vaguely flavored with indignation.

When he had finished his last pipe, Tembarom rose and knocked the ashes out of it.

"Now for Pearson," he said.

He had made up his mind to have a talk with Pearson, and there was no use wasting time. If things didn't suit you, the best thing was to see what you could do to fix them right away — if it wasn't against the law. He went out into the hall, and seeing the two footmen standing waiting, he spoke to them.

"Say, I didn't know you fellows were there," he said. "Are you waiting up for me? Well, you can go to bed, the sooner the quicker. Good night." And he went upstairs whistling.

The glow and richness and ceremonial order of preparation in his bedroom struck him as soon as he
opened the door. Everything which could possibly have
been made ready for his most luxurious comfort
had been made ready. He did not, it is true, care much
for the huge bed with its carved oak canopy and
massive pillars.

"But the lying-down part looks about all right," he
said to himself.

The fine linen, the soft pillow, the downy blankets,
would have allured even a man who was not tired. The
covering had been neatly turned back and the snowy
whiteness opened. That was English, he supposed. They
hadn't got on to that at Mrs. Bowse's.

"But I guess a plain little old New York sleep will
do," he said. "Temple Barholm or no Temple Barholm,
I guess they can't change that."

Then there sounded a quiet knock at the door. He
knew who it would turn out to be, and he was not
mistaken. Pearson stood in the corridor, wearing his
slightly anxious expression, but ready for orders.

Mr. Temple Barholm looked down at him with a
friendly, if unusual, air.

"Say, Pearson," he announced, "if you've come to
wash my face and put my hair up in crimping-pins, you
needn't do it, because I'm not used to it. But come on
in."

If he had told Pearson to enter and climb the
chimney, it cannot be said that the order would have
been obeyed upon the spot, but Pearson would certainly

have hesitated and explained with respectful delicacy that the task was not "his place." He came into the room.

"I came to see, if I could do anything further and —" making a courageous onslaught upon the situation for which he had been preparing himself for hours — "and also — if it is not too late — to venture to trouble you with regard to your wardrobe." He coughed a low, embarrassed cough. "In unpacking, sir, I found — I did not find —"

"You didn't find much, did you?" Tembarom assisted him.

"Of course, sir," Pearson apologized, "leaving New York so hurriedly, your — your man evidently had not time to — er —"

Tembarom looked at him for a few seconds longer, as if making up his mind to something. Then he threw himself easily into the big chair by the fire, and leaned back in it with the frankest and best-natured smile possible.

"I hadn't any man," he said. "Say, Pearson," waving his hand to another chair near by, "suppose you take a seat."

Long and careful training came to Pearson's aid and supported him, but he was afraid that he looked nervous, and certainly there was a lack of entire calm in his voice.

"I — thank you, sir, — I think I'd better stand, sir."

"Why?" inquired Tembarom, taking his tobacco-pouch out of his pocket and preparing to fill another pipe.

"You're most kind, sir, but — but —" in impassioned embarrassment — "I should really *prefer* to stand, sir, if you don't mind. I should feel more — more at 'ome, sir," he added, dropping an h in his agitation.

"Well, if you'd like it better, that's all right," yielded Mr. Temple Barholm, stuffing tobacco into the pipe. Pearson darted to a table, produced a match, struck it, and gave it to him.

"Thank you," said Tembarom, still good-naturedly. "But there are a few things I've *got* to say you *right* now."

Pearson had really done his best, his very best, but he was terrified because of certain circumstances once before referred to.

"I beg pardon, sir," he appealed, "but I am most anxious to give satisfaction in every respect." He *was*, poor young man, horribly anxious. "Today being only the first day, I dare say I have not been all I should have been. I have never valeted an American gentleman before, but I'm sure I shall become accustomed to everything *quite* soon — almost immediately."

"Say," broke in Tembarom, "you're 'way off. I'm not complaining. You're all right."

The easy good temper of his manner was so singularly assuring that Pearson, unexplainable as he found him in every other respect, knew that this at least was to be depended upon, and he drew an almost palpable breath of relief. Something actually allured him into approaching what he had never felt it safe to approach before under like circumstances — a confidential disclosure.

"Thank you, sir: I am most grateful. The — fact is, I

hoped especially to be able to settle in place just now. I — I'm hoping to save up enough to get married, sir."

"You are?" exlaimed Tembarom. "Good business! So was I before all this" — he glanced about him — "fell on top of me."

"I've been saving for three years, sir, and if I can know I'm a permanency — if I can keep this place —"

"You're going to keep it all right," Tembarom cheered him up with. "If you've got an idea you're going to be fired, just you forget it. Cut it right out."

"Is — I beg pardon, sir," Pearson asked with timorous joy, "but is that the American for saying you'll be good enough to keep me on?"

Mr. Temple Barholm thought a second.

"Is 'keep me on' the English for 'let me stay'?"

"Yes, sir."

"Then we're all right. Let's start from there. I'm going to have a heart-to-heart talk with you, Pearson."

"Thank you, sir," said Pearson in a deferential murmur. But if he was not dissatisfied, what was going to happen?

"It'll save us both trouble, and me most. I'm not one of those clever Clarences that can keep up a bluff, making out I know things I don't know. I couldn't deceive a setting hen or a Berlin wool antimacassar."

Pearson swallowed something with effort.

"You see, I fell into this thing *kerchunk,* and I'm just *rattled* — I'm rattled." As Pearson slightly coughed again, he translated for him, "That's American for 'I don't know where I'm at.'"

"Those American jokes, sir, are very funny indeed," answered Pearson, appreciatively.

"Funny!" the new Mr. Temple Barholm exclaimed even aggrievedly. "If you think this lay-out is an American joke to me, Pearson, there's where you're way off. Do you think it a merry jest for a fellow like me to sit up in a high chair in a dining-room like a cathedral and not know whether he ought to bite his own bread or not? And not dare to stir till things are handed to him by five husky footmen? I thought that plain-clothes man was going to cut up my meat, and slap me on the back if I choked."

Pearson's sense of humor was perhaps not inordinate, but unseemly mirth, which he had swallowed at the reference to the setting hen and the Berlin wool antimacassar, momentarily got the better of him, despite his efforts to cough it down, and broke forth in a hoarse, ill-repressed sound.

"I beg pardon, sir," he said with a laudable endeavor to recover his professional bearing. "It's your — American way of expressing it which makes me forget myself. I beg pardon."

Tembarom laughed outright boyishly.

"Oh, cut that out," he said. "Say, how old are you?"

"Twenty-five, sir."

"So am I. If you'd met me three months ago, beating the streets of New York for a living, with holes in my shoes and a celluloid collar on, you'd have looked down on me. I know you would."

"Oh, no, sir," most falsely insisted Pearson.

"Oh, yes, you would," protested Tembarom, cheerfully. "You'd have said I talked through my nose, and I should have laughed at you for dropping your h's. Now you're rattled because I'm Mr. Temple Temple Barholm; but you're not half as rattled as I am."

"You'll get over it, sir, almost immediately," Pearson assured him, hopefully.

"Of course I shall," said Tembarom, with much courage. "But to start right I've got to get over *you*."

"Me, sir?" Pearson breathed anxiously.

"Yes. That's what I want to get off my chest. Now, first off, you came in here to explain to me that, owing to my New York valet having left my New York wardrobe behind, I've not got anything to wear, and so I shall have to buy some clothes."

"I failed to find any dress-shirts, sir," began Pearson, hesitatingly.

Mr. Temple Barholm grinned.

"I always failed to find them myself. I never had a dress-shirt. I never owned a suit of glad rags in my life."

"Gl — glad rags, sir?" stammered Pearson, uncertainly.

"I knew you didn't catch on when I said that to you before dinner. I mean claw-hammer and dress-suit things. Don't you be frightened, Pearson. I never had six good shirts at once, or two pairs of shoes, or more than four ten-cent handkerchiefs at a time since I was born. And when Mr. Palford yanked me away from New York, he didn't suspect a fellow could be in such a state. And I didn't know I was in a state, any how. I was too busy to hunt up people to tell me, because I was rushing something important right through, and I couldn't stop. I just bought the first things I set eyes on and crammed them into my trunk. There, I guess you know the most of this, but you didn't know I knew you knew it. Now you do, and you needn't be afraid to hurt my feelings by telling me I haven't a darned thing I ought to have. You can go straight ahead."

As he leaned back, puffing away at his pipe, he had thrown a leg over the arm of his chair for greater comfort, and it really struck his valet that he had never seen a gentleman more at his ease, even one who *was* one. His casual candidness produced such a relief from the sense of strain and uncertainty that Pearson felt the color returning to his face. An opening had been given him, and it was possible for him to do his duty.

"If you wish, sir, I will make a list," he ventured further, "and the proper firms will send persons to bring things down from London on appro."

"What's 'appro' the English for?"

"Approval, sir."

"Good business! Good old Pearson!"

"Thank you, sir. Shall I attend to it to-night, to be ready for the morning post?"

"In five minutes you shall. But you threw me off the track a bit. The thing I was really going to say was more important than the clothes business."

There was something else, then, thought Pearson, some other unexpected point of view.

"What have you to do for me, anyhow?"

"Valet you, sir."

"That's English for washing my face and combing my hair and putting my socks on, ain't it?"

"Well, sir, it means doing all you require, and being always in attendance when you change."

"How much do you get for it?"

"Thirty shillings a week, sir."

"Say, Pearson," said Tembarom with honest feelings, "I'll give you sixty shillings a week *not* to do it."

Calmed though he had felt a few moments ago, it cannot be denied that Pearson was aghast. How could one be prepared for developments of such an order?

"Not to do it, sir!" he faltered. "But what would the servants think if you had no one to valet you?"

"That's so. What would they think?" But he evidently was not dismayed, for he smiled widely. "I guess the plain-clothes man would throw a fit."

But Pearson's view was more serious and involved a knowledge of not improbable complications. He knew "the hall" and its points of view.

"I couldn't draw my wages, sir," he protested. "There'd be the greatest dissatisfaction among the other servants, sir, if I didn't do my duties. There's always a — a slight jealousy of valets and ladies'-maids. The general idea is that they do very little to earn their salaries. I've seen them fairly hated."

"Is that so? Well, I'll be darned!" remarked Mr. Temple Barholm. He gave a moment to reflection, and then cheered up immensely.

"I'll tell you how we'll fix it. You come up into my

room and bring your tatting or read a newspaper while I dress."He openly chuckled. "Holy smoke! I've *got* to put on my shirt and swear at my collar- buttons myself. If I'm in for having a trained nurse do it for me, it'll give me the Willies. When you danced around me before dinner —"

Pearson's horror forced him to commit the indiscretion of interrupting.

"I hope I didn't *dance*, sir," he implored. "I tried to be extremely quiet."

"That was it," said Tembarom. "I shouldn't have said danced; I meant crept. I kept thinking I should tread on you, and I got so nervous toward the end I thought I should just break down and sob on your bosom and beg to be taken back to home and mother."

"I'm extremely sorry, sir, I am, indeed," apologized Pearson, doing his best not to give way to hysterical giggling. How was a man to keep a decently straight face, and if one didn't, where would it end? One thing after another.

"It was not your fault. It was mine. I haven't a thing against you. You're a first-rate little chap."

"I will try to be more satisfactory to-morrow."

There must be no laughing aloud, even if one burst a blood-vessel. It would not do. Pearson hastily confronted a vision of a young footman or Mr. Burrill himself passing through the corridors on some errand and hearing master and valet shouting together in unseemly and wholly incomprehensible mirth. And the next remark was worse than ever.

"No, you won't, Pearson," Mr. Temple Barholm asserted. "There's where you're wrong. I've got no more use for a valet than I have for a pair of straight-front corsets."

This contained a sobering suggestion.

"But you said, sir, that —"

"Oh, I'm not going to fire you," said Tembarom, generally. "I'll 'keep you on,' but little Willie is going to put on his own socks. If the servants have to be pacified, you come up to my room and do anything you like. Lie on the bed if you want to; get a jew's-harp and play on it — any old thing to pass the time. And I'll raise your wages. What do you say? Is it fixed?"

"I'm here, sir, to do anything you require," Pearson answered distressedly; "but I'm afraid — "

Tembarom's face changed. A sudden thought had struck him.

"I'll tell you one thing you can do," he said; "you can valet that friend of mine."

"Mr. Strangeways, sir?"

"Yes. I've got a notion he wouldn't mind it." He was not joking now. He was in fact suddenly thoughtful.

"Say, Pearson, what do you think of him?"

"Well, sir, I've not seen much of him, and he says very little, but I should think he was a *gentleman,* sir."

Mr. Temple Barholm seemed to think it over.

"That's queer," he said as though to himself. "That's what Ann said." Then aloud, "Would you say he was an American?"

In his unavoidable interest in a matter much talked

over below stairs and productive of great curiosity Pearson was betrayed. He could not explain to himself, after he had spoken, how he could have been such a fool as to forget; but forget himself and the birthplace of the new Mr. Temple Barholm he did.

"Oh, no, sir," he exlaimed hastily; "he's *quite* the gentleman, sir, even though he is queer in his mind." The next instant he caught himself and turned cold. An American or a Frenchman or an Italian, in fact, a native of any country on earth so slighted with an unconsciousness so natural, if he had been a man of hot temper, might have thrown something at him or kicked him out of the room; but Mr. Temple Barholm took his pipe out of his mouth and looked at him with a slow, broadening smile.

"Would you call me a gentleman, Pearson?" he asked.

Of course there was no retrieving such a blunder, Pearson felt, but —

"Certainly, sir," he stammered. "Most — most *certainly,* sir."

"Pearson," said Tembarom, shaking his head slowly, with a grin so good-natured that even the frankness of his words was friendly humor itself — "Pearson, you're a liar. But that doesn't jolt me a bit. I dare say I'm not one, anyhow. We might put an 'ad' in one of your papers and find out."

"I — I beg your pardon, sir," murmured Pearson in actual anguish of mind.

Mr. Temple Barholm laughed outright.

"Oh, I've not got it in for you. How could you help

it?" he said. Then he stopped joking again. "If you want to please *me*," he added with deliberation, "you look after Mr. Strangeways, and don't let anything disturb him. Don't bother him, but just find out what he wants. When he gets restless, come and tell me. If I'm out, tell him I'm coming back. Don't let him worry. You understand — don't let him worry."

"I'll do my best — my very best, sir," Pearson answered devoutly. "I've been nervous and excited this first day because I am so anxious to please — everything seems to depend on it just now," he added, daring another confidential outburst. "But you'll see I do know how to keep my wits about me in general, and I've got a good memory, and I have learned my duties, sir. I'll attend to Mr. Strangeways most particular."

As Tembarom listened, and watched his neat, blond countenance, and noted the undertone of quite desperate appeal in his low voice, he was thinking of a number of things. Chiefly he was thinking of little Ann Hutchinson and the Harlem flat which might have been "run" on fifteen dollars a week.

"I want to know I have some one in this museum of a place who'll *understand*," he said — "some one who'll do just exactly what I say and ask no fool questions and keep his mouth shut. I believe you could do it."

"I'll swear I could, sir. Trust me," was Pearson's astonishingly emotional and hasty answer.

"I'm going to," returned Mr. Temple Barholm. "I've set my mind on putting something through in my own way. It's a queer thing, and most people would say I was a fool for trying it. Mr. Hutchinson does, but Miss Hutchinson doesn't."

There was a note in his tone of saying "Miss Hutchinson doesn't" which opened up vistas to Pearson — strange vistas when one thought of old Mrs. Hutchinson's cottage and the estate of Temple Barholm.

"We're just about the same age," his employer continued, "and in a sort of way we're in just about the same fix."

Their eyes looked into each other's a second; but it was not for Pearson to presume to make any comment whatsoever upon the possible nature of "the fix." Two or three more puffs, and Mr. Temple Barholm spoke again.

"Say, Pearson, I don't want to butt in, but what about that little bunch of calico of yours — the one you're saving up for?"

"Calico, sir?" said Pearson, at sea, but hopeful. Whatsoever the new Mr. Temple Barholm meant, one began to realize that it was not likely to be unfriendly.

"That's American for *her*, Pearson. 'Her' stands for the same thing both in English and American, I guess. What's her name and where is she? Don't say a word if you don't want to."

Pearson drew a step nearer. There was an extraordinary human atmosphere in the room which caused things to begin to go on in his breast. He had had a harder life than Tembarom because he had been more timid and less buoyant and less unselfconscious. He had been beaten by a drunken mother and kicked by a drunken father. He had gone hungry and faint to the board school and had been punished as a dull boy. After he had struggled into a place as page, he had been bullied by footmen and had had his ears boxed by cooks and butlers. Ladies'-maids and smart housemaids had sneered at him, and made him feel himself a hopeless, vulgar little worm who would never "get on." But he had got on, in a measure, because he had worked like a slave and openly resented nothing. A place like this had been his fevered hope and dream from his page days, though of course his imagination had not encompassed attendance on a gentleman who had never owned a dress-shirt in his life. Yet gentleman or no gentleman, he was a Temple Barholm, and there was something about him, something human in his young voice and grin and queer, unheard-of New York jokes, which Pearson had never encountered, and which had the effect of making him feel somehow more of a man than his timorous nature had ever allowed of his feeling before. It suggested that they were both, valet and master, merely masculine human creatures of like kind. The way he had said "Miss Hutchinson" and the twinkle in his eye when he'd made that American joke about the "little bunch of calico"! The curious fact was that thin, neat white-blooded-looking Pearson was passionately in love. So he took the step nearer and grew hot and spoke low.

"Her name is Rose Merrick, sir, and she's in place in London. She's lady's-maid to a lady of title, and it isn't an easy place. Her lady has a high temper, and she's economical with her servants. Her maid has to sew early and late, and turn out as much as if she was a whole dressmaking establishment. She's clever with her needle, and it would be easier if she felt it was appreciated. But she's treated haughty and severe, though she tries her very best. She has to wait up half the night after balls, and I'm afraid it's breaking her spirit and her health. That's why, — I beg your pardon, sir," he added, his voice shaking — "that's why I'd bear anything on earth if I could give her a little home of her own."

"Gee whizz!" ejaculated Mr. Temple Barholm, with feeling. "I guess you would!"

"And that's not all, sir," said Pearson. "She's a beautiful girl, sir, with a figure, and service is sometimes not easy for a young woman like that. His lordship — the master of the house, sir, — is much too attentive. He's a man with bad habits; the last lady's-maid was sent away in disgrace. Her ladyship wouldn't believe she hadn't been forward when she saw things she didn't like, though every one in the hall knew the girl hated his bold ways with her, and her mother nearly broke her heart. He's begun with Rose, and it just drives me mad, sir, it does!"

He choked, and wiped his forehead with his clean handkerchief. It was damp, and his young eyes had fire in them, as Mr. Temple Barholm did not fail to observe.

"I'm taking a liberty talking to you like this, sir," he said. "I'm behaving as if I didn't know my place, sir."

"Your place is behind that fellow, kicking him till he'll never sit down again except on eider-down cushions three deep," remarked Mr. Temple Barholm, with fire in his eyes also. "That's where your place is. It's where mine would be if I was in the same house with him and caught him making a goat of himself. I bet nine Englishmen out of ten would break his darned neck for him if they got on to his little ways, even if they were lordships themselves."

"The decent ones won't know," Pearson said. "That's not what happens, sir. He can laugh and chaff it off with her ladyship and coax her round. But a girl that's discharged like that, Rose says, that's the worst of it: she says she's got a character fastened on to her for life that no respectable man ought to marry her with."

Mr. Temple Barholm removed his leg from the arm of his chair and got up. Long-legged, sinewy, but somewhat slouchy in his badly made tweed suit, sharp New York face and awful American style notwithstanding, he still looked rather nice as he laid his hand on his valet's shoulder and gave him a friendly push.

"See here," he said. "What you've got to say to Rose is that she's just got to cut that sort of thing out — cut it right out. Talking to a man that's in love with her as if he was likely to throw her down because lies were told. Tell her to forget it — forget it quick. Why, what does she suppose a man's *for*, by jinks? What's he *for*?"

"I've told her that, sir, though of course not in American. I just swore it on my knees in Hyde Park one night when she got out for an hour. But she laid her poor head on the back of the bench and cried and wouldn't listen. She says she cares for me too much to —"

Tembarom's hand clutched his shoulder. His face lighted and glowed suddenly.

"Care for you too much," he asked. "Did she say that? God bless her!"

"That's what I said," broke in Pearson.

"I heard another girl say that — just before I left New York — a girl that's just a wonder," said his master. "A girl can be a wonder, can't she?"

"Rose is, sir," protested Pearson. "She is, indeed sir. And her eyes are that blue —"

"Blue, are they?" interrupted Tembarom. "I know the kind. I'm on to the whole thing. And what's more, I'm going to fix it. You tell Rose — and tell her from me — that she's going to leave that place, and you're going to stay in this one, and — well, presently things'll begin to happen. They're going to be all right — *all right*," he went on, with immensely convincing emphasis. "She's going to have that little home of her own." He paused a moment for reflection, and then a sudden thought presented itself to him. "Why, darn it!" he exclaimed, "there must be a whole raft of little homes that belong to me in one place or another. Why couldn't I fix you both up in one of them?"

"Oh, sir!" Pearson broke forth in some slight alarm. He went so fast and so far all in a moment. And Pearson really possessed a neat, well-ordered conscience, and, moreover, "knew his place." "I hope I didn't seem to be expecting you to trouble yourself about me, sir. I mustn't presume on your kindness."

"It's not kindness; it's — well, it's just human. I'm

going to think this thing over. You just keep your hair on, and let me do my own valeting, and you'll see I'll fix it for you somehow."

What he thought of doing, how he thought of doing it, and what Pearson was to expect, the agitated young man did not know. The situation was of course abnormal, judged by all respectable, long-established custom. A man's valet and his valet's "young woman" were not usually of intimate interest. Gentlemen were sometimes "kind" to you — gave you half a sovereign or even a sovereign, and perhaps asked after your mother if you were supporting one; but —

"I never dreamed of going so far, sir," he said. "I forgot myself, I'm afraid."

"Good thing you did. It's made me feel as if we were brothers." He laughed again, enjoying the thought of the little thing who cared for Pearson "too much" and had eyes that were "that blue." Say, I've just thought of something else. Have you bought her an engagement-ring yet?"

"No, sir. In our class of life jewelry is beyond the means."

"I just wondered," Mr. Temple Barholm said. He seemed to be thinking of something that pleased him as he fumbled for his pocket-book and took a clean bank-note out of it. "I'm not on to what the value of this thing is in real money, but you go and buy her a ring with it, and I bet she'll be so pleased you'll have the time of your life."

Pearson taking it, and recognizing its value in *un*real

money, was embarrassed by feeling the necessity of explanation.

"This is a five-pound note, sir. It's too much, sir, it is, indeed. This would *furnish the front parlor.*" He said it almost solmenly.

Mr. Temple Barholm looked at the note interestedly.

"Would it? By jinks!" and his laugh had a certain softness of recollection. "I guess that's just what Ann would say. She'd know what it would furnish, you bet your life!"

"I'm most grateful, sir," protested Pearson, "but I oughtn't to take it. Being an American gentleman and not accustomed to British money, you don't realize that —"

"I'm not accustomed to any kind of money," said his master. "I'm scared to be left alone in the room with it. That's what's the matter. If I don't give some away, I shall never know I've got it. Cheer up, Pearson. You take that and buy the ring, and when you start furnishing, I'll see you don't get left."

"I don't know what to say, sir," Pearson faltered emotionally. "I don't indeed."

"Don't say a darn thing," replied Mr. Temple Barholm. And just here his face changed as Mr. Palford had seen it change before, and as Pearson often saw it change later. His New York jocular irreverence dropped from him, and he looked mature and oddly serious.

"I've tried to sort of put you wise to the way I've lived and the things I *haven't* had ever since I was born," he said, "but I guess you don't really know a thing about it. I've got more money coming in every year than a thousand of me would ever expect to see in their lives, according to my calculation. And I don't know how to do any of the things a fellow who is what you call 'a gentleman' would know how to do. I mean in the way of spending it. Now, I've got to get some fun out of it. I should be a mutt if I didn't, so I'm going to spend it my own way. I may make about seventy-five different kinds of a fool of myself, but I guess I shan't do any particular harm."

"You'll do good, sir, — to every one."

"Shall I?" said Tembarom, speculatively. "Well, I'm not exactly setting out with that in my mind. I'm no Young Men's Christian Association, but I'm not in for doing harm, anyway. You take your five-pound note — come to think of it, Palford said it came to about twenty-five dollars, real money. Hully gee! I never thought I'd have twenty-five dollars to *give away*! It makes me feel like I was Morgan."

"Thank you, sir; thank you," said Pearson, putting the note in his pocket with rapt gratitude in his neat face. "You — you do not wish me to remain — to do anything for you?"

"Not a thing. But just go and find out if Mr. Strange-ways is asleep. If he isn't and seems restless, I'll come and have a talk with him."

"Yes, sir," said Pearson, and went at once.

10. THE RAPID-FIRE LORGNON IS SPIKED

from *The Spenders* [Chapt. VII]
by Harry Leon Wilson, 1902

By 1900 not only had Americans convinced themselves that they were a breed entirely different from Englishmen, but also they were on the way to convincing themselves that there were distinct and recognizable breeds within America. Indeed, a New Yorker and a Montanan were pictured as being at spiritual poles almost more widely separated than were those of London and New York. This game dated back to the eighteenth century, when Royall Tyler's The Contrast *first put a Yankee upon the stage. There had followed scores of novels, plays, and brief sketches in newspapers and magazines which over the years had developed familiar "types" — the Western frontiersman, the shrewd Yankee, the plantation Negro. Eventually, in works like Mark Twain's* Huckleberry Finn, *characters reminiscent of these types found their way into literature.*

In Ruggles of Red Gap *Harry Leon Wilson worked two popular veins: climbers vs. non-climbers, and*

English butler vs. cow town. In his less well known The Spenders, *subtitled "A Tale of the Third Generation," Wilson concentrated on the East-West schism. If his delineation of the two breeds is extreme, apparently the audience which greeted the book in 1902 welcomed just such exaggeration.*

The mother of the Eastern girl must, of course, wear a "lorgnon," and in this chapter the "lorgnon" is spiked as soon as mother discovers that the young man whom she had taken for a Western miner is actually the owner of the mine. Percival Bines, that third-generation mine owner, has been reluctantly inspecting the property which his father's sudden death had recently brought into his hands. He hated to leave New York in order to make the trip; but the pleas of his grandfather, old Uncle Peter, whose prospecting had laid the foundation for the Bines mining empire, have prevailed. Uncle Peter, who never gets east of Cheyenne, assumes that no man can long resist the appeal of the West, and that surely all his grandson needs is one trip through the Bines empire to see the error of his ways in clinging to an Eastern life, now that he has finished his course at Harvard. As the chapter opens, Percival is speaking to his grandfather in a cross-cut of the "One Girl" mine, where a party of Easterners has stopped for a brief visit during a railroad trip across the continent. The visitors have mistaken the Bineses for miners, a fact which pleases Percival, since it allows him to conduct the girl in the party, Avice Milbrey, on a private tour of inspection through the mine.

He found Uncle Pete in the cross-cut, studying a bit of ore through a glass, and they went back to ascend.

"Them folks," said the old man, "must be the kind that newspaper meant, that had done something in practical achievement. I bet that girl's mother will achieve something practical with you fur cuttin' the girl out of the bunch; she was awful tormented; talked two or three times about the people in the humbler walks of life bein' strangely something or other. You ain't such a humble walker now, are you, son? But say, that yellow-haired woman, she ain't a bit diffident, is she? She's a very hearty lady, I *must* say!"

"But did you see Miss Milbrey?"

"Oh, that's her name is it, the one that her mother was so worried about and you? Yes, I saw her. Peart and cunnin', but a heap too wise fur you, son; take my steer on that. Say, she'd have your pelt nailed to the barn while you was wonderin' which way you'd jump."

"Oh, I know I'm only a tender, teething infant," the young man answered, with masterly satire.

"Well, now, as long's you got that bank roll you jest look out fur cupboard love — the kind the old cat has when she comes rubbin' up against your leg and purrin' like you was the whole thing."

The young man smiled, as they went up, with youth's godlike faith in its own sufficiency, albeit he smarted from the slights put upon him.

At the surface a pleasant shock was in store for him. There stood the formidable Mrs. Milbrey beaming upon him. Behind her was Mr. Milbrey, the pleasing model of all a city's refinements, awaiting the boon of a handclasp. Behind these were the uncomfortable little man, the chatty blonde, and the two solemn young men who had lately exhibited more manner than manners. Percival felt they were all regarding him now with affectionate concern. They pressed forward effusively.

"*So* good of you, Mr. Bines, to take an interest in us — my daughter has been so anxious to see one of these fascinating mines." "Awfully obliged, Mr. Bines." "Charmed, old man; deuced pally of you to stay by us down in that hole, you know." "So clever of you to know where to find the gold —"

He lost track of the speakers. Their speeches became one concerted effusion of affability that was music to his ears.

Miss Milbrey was apart from the group. Having doffed the waterproofs, she was now pluming herself with those fussy-looking but mysteriously potent little pats which restore the attire and mind of women to their normal perfection and serenity. Upon her face was still the amused look Percival had noted below.

"And, Mr. Bines, do come in with that quaint old grandfather of yours and lunch with us," urged Mrs. Milbrey, who had, as it were, spiked her lorgnon.

"Here's Mr. Shepler to second the invitation — and then we shall chat about this very interesting West."

Miss Milbrey nodded encouragement, seeming to chuckle inwardly.

In the spacious dining compartment of the Shepler car the party was presently at lunch.

"You seem so little like a Western man," Mrs. Milbrey confided graciously to Percival on her right.

"We cal'late he'll fetch out all straight, though, in a year or so," put in Uncle Peter, from over his chop, with guileless intent to defend his grandson from what he believed to be an attack. "Of course a young man's bound to get some foolishness into him in an Eastern College like this boy went to."

Percival had flushed at the compliment to himself; also at the old man's failure to identify it as such.

Mr. Milbrey caressed his glass of claret with ardent eyes and took the situation in hand with the easy confidence of a master.

"The West," said he, affably, "has sent us some magnificent men. In truth, it's amazing to take count of the Western men among us in all the professions. They are notable, perhaps I should say, less for deliberate niceties of style than for a certain rough directness, but so adaptable is the American character that one frequently does not suspect their — er — humble origin."

"Meaning their Western origin?" inquired Shepler, blandly, with secret intent to brew strife.

"Well — er — to be sure, my dear fellow, not

necessarily humble, — of course — perhaps I should have said —"

"Of course, not necessarily disgraceful, as you say, Milbrey," interrupted Shepler, "and they often do conceal it. Why, I know a chap in New York who was positively never east of Kansas City until he was twenty-five or so, and yet that fellow to-day" — he lowered his voice to the pitch of impressiveness — "has over eighty pairs of trousers and complains of the hardship every time he has to go to Boston."

"Fancy, now!" exclaimed Mrs. Drelmer, the blonde. Mr Milbrey looked slightly puzzled and Uncle Peter chuckled, affirming mentally that Rulon Shepler must be like one of those tug-boats, with most of his lines under the surface.

"But, I say, you know, Shepler," protested one of the solemn young men, "he must still talk like a banjo."

"And gargle all his 'r's,'" added the other, very earnestly. "They never get over that, you know."

"Instead of losin' 'em entirely," put in Uncle Peter, who found himself feeling what his grandson called "Westy." "Of course, he calls it 'Ne' Yawk,' and prob'ly he don't like it in Boston because they always call 'em 'rawroystahs.'"

"Good for the old boy!" thought Percival, and then, aloud: "It *is* hard for the West and the East to forgive each other's dialects. The inflated 'r' and the smothered 'r' never quite harmonise."

"Western money talks good straight New York talk," ventured Miss Milbrey, with the air of one who had observed in her time.

Shepler grinned, and the parents of the young woman resisted with indifferent success their twin impulses to frown.

"But the service is so wretched in the West," suggested Oldaker, the carefully dressed little man with the tired, troubled eyes, whom the world had been deprived of. "I fancy, now, there's not a good waiter this side of New York."

"An American," said Percival, "never can make a good waiter or a good valet. It takes a Latin, or, still better, a Briton, to feel the servility required for good service of that sort. An American, now, always fails at it because he knows he is as good as you are, and he knows that you know it, and there you are, two mirrors of American equality face to face and reflecting each other endlessly, and neither is comfortable. The American is as uncomfortable at having certain services performed for him by another American as the other in performing them. Give him a Frenchman or an Italian or a fellow born within the sound of Bow Bells to clean his boots and lay out his things and serve his dinner and he's all right enough."

"Hear, hear!" cried Uncle Peter.

"Fancy, now," said Mrs. Drelmer, "a creature in a waiter's jacket having emotions of that sort!"

"Our excellent country," said Mr. Milbrey, "is perhaps not yet what it will be; there is undeniably a most distressing rawness where we might expect finish. Now in Chicago," he continued in a tone suitably hushed for the relation of occult phenomena, "we dined with a person who served champagne with the oysters, soup, fish, and *entrée*, and for the remainder of the dinner — you may credit me or not — he proffered a claret of 1875 — I need hardly remind you, the most delicate vintage of the latter half of the century — and it was served *frappé*." There was genuine emotion in the speaker's voice.

"And papa nearly swooned when our host put cracked ice and two lumps of sugar into his own glass —"

"*Avice, dear!*" remonstrated the father in a tone implying that some things positively must not be mentioned at table.

"Well, you shouldn't expect too much of those self-made men in Chicago," said Shepler.

"If they'd only make themselves as well as they make their sausages and things," sighed Mr. Milbrey.

"And the self-made man will talk shop," suggested Oldaker. "He thinks you're dying to hear how he made the first thousand of himself."

"Still, those Chicago chaps learn quickly enough when they settle in New York," ventured one of the young men.

"I knew a Chicago chap who lived East two years and went back not a half bad sort," said the other. "God help him now, though; his father made him go back to work in a butcher shop or something of the sort."

"Best thing I ever heard about Chicago," said Uncle Peter, "a man from your town told me once he had to stay in Chicago a year, and, says he, 'I went out there a New Yorker, and I went home an American,' he says."

The old man completed this anecdote in tones that were slightly inflamed.

"How extremely typical!" said Mrs. Milbrey "Truly the West is the place of unspoiled Americanism and the great unspent forces; you are quite right, Mr. Bines."

"Think of all the unspent forces back in that silver mine," remarked Miss Milbrey, with a patent effort to be significant.

"My perverse child delights to pose as a sordid young woman," the fond mother explained to Percival, "yet no one could be less so, and you, Mr. Bines, I am sure, would be the last to suspect her of it. I saw in you at once those sterling qualities —"

"Isn't it dreadfully dark down in that sterling silver mine?" observed Miss Milbrey, apropos of nothing, apparently, while her mother attacked a second chop that she had meant not to touch.

"Here's hoping we'll soon be back in God's own country," said Oldaker, raising his glass.

"Hear, hear!" cried Uncle Peter, and drained his glass eagerly as they drank the toast. Whereat they all laughed, and Mrs. Drelmer said, "What a dear, lively wit, for an old gentleman."

"Oldaker," said Shepler, "has really been the worst sufferer. This is his first trip West."

"Beg pardon, Shepler! I was West as far as Buffalo — let me see — in 1878 or '79."

"Dear me! is that so?" queried Uncle Peter. "I got East as fur as Cheyenne that same year. We nearly run into each other, didn't we?"

Shepler grinned again.

"Oldaker found a man from New York on the train the other day, up in one of the emigrant cars. He was a truck driver, and he looked it and talked it, but Oldaker stuck by him all the afternoon."

"Well, he'd left the old town three weeks after I had, and he'd been born there the same year I was — in the Ninth ward — and he remembered as well as I did the day Barnum's museum burned at Broadway and Ann. I liked to hear him talk. Why, it was a treat just to hear him say Broadway and Twenty-third street, or Madison Square or City Hall Park. The poor devil had consumption, too, and probably he'll never see them again. I don't know if I shall ever have it, but I'd never leave the old town as he was doing."

"That's like Billy Brue," said Uncle Peter. "Billy loves faro bank jest as this gentleman loves New York. When he gets a roll he *has* to play. One time he landed in Pocatello when there wa'n't but one game in town. Billy found it and started in. A friend saw him there and called out. 'Billy,' says he, 'cash in and come out; that's a brace game.' 'Sure?' says Billy. 'Sure,' says the feller. 'All right,' says Billy, 'much obliged fur puttin' me on.' And he started out lookin' fur another game. About two hours later the feller saw Billy comin' out of the same place and Billy owned up he'd gone back and blowed in every cent. 'Why, you geezer,' says his friend, 'didn't I put you on that they was dealin' brace there?' 'Sure,' says Billy, 'sure you did. But what could I do? It was the only game in town!'"

"That New York mania is the same sort," said

Shepler, laughing, while Mrs. Drelmer requested everybody to fancy immediately.

"Your grandfather is *so* dear and quaint," said Mrs. Milbrey; "you must certainly bring him to New York with you, for of course a young man of your capacity and graces will never be satisfied out of New York."

"Young men like yourself are assuredly needed there," remarked Mr. Milbrey, warmly.

"Surely they are," agreed Miss Milbrey, and yet with a manner that seemed almost to annoy both parents. They were sparing no opportunity to make the young man conscious of his real oneness with those about him, and yet subtly to intimate that people of just the Milbreys' perception were required to divine it at present.

"These Westerners fancy you one of themselves, I dare say," Mrs. Milbrey had said, and the young man purred under the strokings. His fever for the East was back upon him. His weeks with Uncle Peter going over the fields where his father had prevailed had made him convalescent, but these New Yorkers — the very manner and atmosphere of them — undid the work. He envied them their easier speech, their matter-of-fact air of omniscience, the elaborate and cultivated simplicity of their dress, their sureness and sufficiency in all that they thought and said and did. He was homesick again for the life he had glimpsed. The West was rude, desolate, and depressing. Even Uncle Peter, whom he had come warmly to admire, jarred upon him with his crudity and his Western assertiveness.

And there was the woman of the East, whose presence had made the day to seem dream-like; and she was kind, which was more than he would have dared to hope, and her people, after their first curious chill of indifference, seemed actually to be courting him. She, the fleeting and impalpable dream-love, whom the thought of seeing over again had been wildly absurd, was now a human creature with a local habitation, the most beautiful name in the world, and two parents whose complaisance was obvious even through the lover's timidity.

11. FIRE-LIGHT TALKS IN MY GRAND-MOTHER'S KITCHEN

from *Oldtown Folks* [Chapt. VI]
by Harriet Beecher Stowe, 1869

A glance at any American magazine, Christmas gift book, college reading list, even newspaper of a century ago will indicate to what an extent American readers found religion a subject of major interest and concern. What Harriet Beecher Stowe has called the "sort of half Hebrew theocracy, half ultra-democratic republic" was disappearing, and although the rest of the country had never shared New England's absorption in theology and religion, Sunday was still a day different from the other six, for more reasons than closed stores, and people knew Bible stories and Pilgrim's Progress. *In the secular decades which have followed, even Americans have tended to label large sections of earlier American history, and large areas of the country in those earlier times as simply "religious," losing sight of the rich variety of opinions and people who lived within the religious framework — a variety almost as rich as that which lived within Chaucer's Christian world.*

Harriet Beecher Stowe did more than write Uncle Tom's Cabin. *She wrote, also, a number of novels and tales which should be prescribed reading for anyone who thinks that Puritans were all alike, and were all grim. One of the most attractive of these stories is* Oldtown Folks, *an account of the life of a Massachusetts village in post-Revolutionary days, when men of substance in the town still wore knee breeches, silk stockings, and shoe buckles, and when the theology of Jonathan Edwards was a quite literally burning issue for many people. Yet one of the great interests of the book is how wide a divergence of opinion and practice there could be on matters both theological and social under one Puritan roof in Oldtown.*

The chapter given here shows that the kitchen of Old Deacon Badger, a farmer and miller of substance, was big enough to hold the deacon himself, who leaned toward the relatively liberal Arminian teachings which softened the doctrine of predestination; the deacon's wife, a true Calvinist who was anything but grim; their college son, Bill, inclined to be gay about matters theological or social; and all shades of questioners and believers between. It was, also, large enough to hold Major Broad and Miss Mehitable Rossiter, at one end of the social scale, and the two old wandering Indian women, Betty Poganut and Sally Wonsamug, plus Sam Lawson, town handyman who managed to be shiftless despite a shrewish wife, at the other. Let no one assume that the thorough political democracy of the village made it classless, yet Miss Mehitable and Indian Betty shared the same kitchen as easily as Chaucer's Knight and the drunken miller shared the same pilgrimage. Perhaps, as in the case of Chaucer's goodly company, Oldtown folks' consciousness of being part of one Christian universe had something to do with this fellowship.

The "I" of the story is Horace Holyoke, a little boy whose schoolteacher-father has just died of overwork in pursuit of learning. The boy has come, with his mother and brother, back to the grandfather's hospitable roof.

My grandmother's kitchen was a great, wide, roomy apartment, whose white-sanded floor was always as clean as hands could make it. It was resplendent with the sheen of a set of scoured pewter plates and platters, which stood arranged on a dresser on one side. The great fireplace swept quite across another side. There we burned cord-wood, and the fire was built up on architectural principles known to those days. First came an enormous back-log, rolled in with the strength of two men, on the top of which was piled a smaller log; and then a fore-stick, of a size which would entitle it to rank as a log in our times, went to make the front foundation of the fire. The rearing of the ample pile thereupon was a matter of no small architectural skill, and all the ruling members of our family circle had their own opinions about its erection, which they maintained with the zeal and pertinacity which become earnest people. My grandfather, with his grave smile, insisted that he was the only reasonable fire-builder of the establishment; but when he had arranged his sticks in the most methodical order, my grandmother would be sure to rush out with a thump here and a twitch there, and diverse incoherent exclamations tending to imply that men never know how to build a fire. Frequently her intense zeal for immediate effect would end in a general rout and roll of the sticks in all directions, with puffs of smoke down the chimney, requiring the setting open of the outside door; and then Aunt Lois would come to the rescue, and, with a face severe with determination, tear down the whole structure and rebuild from the foundation with exactest precision, but with an air that cast volumes of contempt on all that had gone before. The fact is, that there is no little nook of domestic life which gives snug harbor to so much self-will and self-righteousness as the family hearth; and this is particularly the case with wood fires, because, from the miscellaneous nature of the material, and the sprightly activity of the combustion, there is a constant occasion for tending and alteration, and so a vast field for individual opinion.

We had come home from our second Sunday service. Our evening meal of smoking brown bread and baked beans had been discussed, and the supper-things washed and put out of sight. There was an uneasy, chill moaning and groaning out of doors showing the coming up of an autumn storm, — just enough chill and wind to make the brightness of a social hearth desirable, — and my grandfather had built one of his most methodical and splendid fires.

The wide, ample depth of the chimney was aglow in all its cavernous length with the warm leaping light that burst out in lively jets and spirts from every rift and chasm. The great black crane that swung over it, with its multiplicity of pot-hooks and trammels, seemed to have a sort of dusky illumination, like that of old Caesar's black, shining face, as he sat on his block of wood in the deep recess of the farther corner, with his hands on the knees of his Sunday pantaloons, gazing lovingly into the blaze with all the devotion of a fire-worshipper. On week-day evenings old Caesar used to have his jack-knife in active play in this corner, and whistles and pop-guns and squirrel-traps for us youngsters grew under his plastic hand; but on Sunday evening he was too good a Christian even to think of a jack-knife, and if his hand casually encountered it in his pocket, he resisted it as a temptation of the Devil, and sat peacefully winking and blinking, and occasionally breaking out into a ripple of private giggles which appeared to spring purely from the overflow of bodily contentment. My Uncle Bill was in that condition which is peculiarly apt to manifest itself in the youth of well-conducted families on Sunday evenings, — a kind of friskiness of spirits which appears to be a reactionary state from the spiritual tension of the day, inclining him to skirmish and threatening every minute to burst out into most unbecoming uproariousness. This state among the youngsters of a family on Sunday evening is a familiar trial of all elders who have had the task of keeping them steady during the sacred hours.

My Uncle Bill, in his week-day frame, was the wit and buffoon of the family, — an adept in every art that could shake the sides, and bring a laugh out on the gravest face. His features were flexible, his powers of grimace and story-telling at times irresistible. On the present occasion it was only my poor mother's pale, sorrowful face that kept him in any decent bounds. He did not wish to hurt his sister's feelings, but he was boiling over with wild and selfish impulses, which he vented now by a sly tweak at the cat's tail, then by a surreptitious dig at black Caesar's sides which made the poor black a helpless, quivering mass of giggle, and then he would slyly make eyes and mouths at Bill and me behind Aunt Lois's chair, which almost slew us with laughter, though all the while he appeared with painful effort to keep on a face of portentous gravity.

On the part of Aunt Lois, however, there began to be manifested unequivocal symptoms that it was her will and pleasure to have us all leave our warm fireside and establish ourselves in the best room, — for we had a best room, else wherefore were we on tea-drinking terms with the high aristocracy of Oldtown? We had our best room, and kept it as cold, as uninviting and stately, as devoid of human light or warmth, as the most fashionable shut-up parlor of modern days. It had the tallest and brightest pair of brass andirons conceivable, and a shovel and tongs to match, that were so heavy that the mere lifting them was work enough, without doing anything with them. It had also a bright-varnished mahogany tea-table, over which was a looking-glass in a gilt frame, with a row of little architectural balls on it; which looking-glass was always kept shrouded in white muslin at all seasons of the year, on account of a tradition that flies might be expected to attack it for one or two weeks in summer. But truth compels me to state, that I never saw or heard of a fly whose heart could endure Aunt Lois's parlor. It was so dark, so cold, so still, that all that frisky, buzzing race, who delight in air and sunshine, universally deserted and seceded from it; yet the looking-glass, and occasionally the fire-irons, were rigorously shrouded, as if desperate attacks might any moment be expected.

Now the kitchen was my grandmother's own room. In one corner of it stood a round table with her favorite books, her great workbasket, and by it a rickety rocking-chair, the bottom of which was of ingenious domestic manufacture, being in fact made by interwoven strips of former coats and pantaloons of the home circle; but a most comfortable and easy seat it made. My grandfather had also a large splint-bottomed arm-chair, with rockers to it, in which he swung luxuriously in the corner of the great fireplace. By the side of its ample blaze we sat down to our family meals, and afterwards, while grandmother and Aunt Lois washed up the tea-things, we all sat and chatted by the firelight. Now it was a fact that nobody liked to sit in the best room. In the kitchen each member of the family had established unto him or her self some little pet private snuggery, some chair or stool, some individual nook, — forbidden to gentility, but dear to the ungenteel natural heart, — that we looked back to regretfully when we were banished to the colder regions of the best room.

There the sitting provisions were exactly one dozen stuffed-seated cherry chairs, with upright backs and griffin feet, each foot terminating in a bony claw, which resolutely grasped a ball. These chairs were high and slippery, and preached decorum in the very attitudes which they necessitated, as no mortal could ever occupy them except in the exercise of a constant and collected habit of mind.

Things being thus, when my Uncle Bill saw Aunt Lois take up some coals on a shovel, and look towards the best-room door, he came and laid his hand on hers directly, with, "Now, Lois, what are you going to do?"

"Going to make up a fire in the best room."

"Now, Lois, I protest. You're not going to do any such thing. Hang grandeur and all that.

' 'Mid pleasures and palaces though we may roam,
 Be it ever so humble, there's no place like home,'

you know; and home means right here by mother's kitchen-fire, where she and father sit, and want to sit. You know nobody ever wants to go into that terrible best room of yours."

"Now, Bill, how you talk!" said Aunt Lois, smiling, and putting down her shovel.

"But then, you see," she said, the anxious cloud again settling down on her brow, — "you see, we're exposed to calls, and who knows who may come in? I shouldn't wonder if Major Broad, or Miss Mehitable, might drop in, as they saw you down from College."

"Let 'em come; never fear. They all know we've got a best room, and that's enough. Or, if you'd rather, I'll pin a card to that effect upon the door; and then we'll take our ease. Or, better than that, I'll take 'em all in and show 'em our best chairs, andirons, and mahogany table, and then we can come out and be comfortable."

"Bill, you're a saucy boy," said Aunt Lois, looking at him indulgently as she subsided into her chair.

"Yes, that he always was," said my grandfather, with a smile of the kind that fathers give to frisky sophomores in college.

"Well, come sit down, anyway," said my grandmother, "and let's have a little Sunday-night talk."

"Sunday-night talk, with all my heart," said Bill, as he seated himself comfortably right in front of the cheerful blaze. "Well, it must be about 'the meetin',' of course. Our old meeting-house looks as elegant as ever. Of all the buildings I ever saw to worship any kind of a being in, that meeting-house certainly is the most extraordinary. It really grows on me every time I come home!"

"Come, now, Bill," said Aunt Lois.

"Come, now! Ain't I coming? Haven't said anything but what you all know. Said our meeting-house was extraordinary, and you all know it is; and there's extraordinary folks in it. I don't believe so queer a tribe could be mustered in all the land of Israel as we congregate. I hope some of our oddities will be in this evening after cider. I need to study a little, so that I can give representations of nature in our club at Cambridge. Nothing like going back to nature, you know. Old Obscue, seems to me, was got up in fine fancy this morning; and Sam Lawson had an extra touch of the hearse about him. Hepsy must have been disciplining him this morning, before church. I always know when Sam is fresh from a matrimonial visitation: he's peculiarly pathetic about the gills at those times. Why don't Sam come in here?"

"I'm sure I hope he won't," said Aunt Lois. "One reason why I wanted to sit in the best room to-night was that every old tramper and queer object sees the light of our kitchen fire, and comes in for a lounge and a drink; and then, when one has genteel persons calling, it makes it unpleasant."

"O, we all know you're aristocratic, Lois: but, you see, you can't be indulged. You must have your purple and fine linen and your Lazarus at the gate come together some time, just as they do in the meeting-house and the graveyard. Good for you all, if not agreeable."

Just at this moment the conversation was interrupted by a commotion in the back sink-room, which sounded much like a rush of a flight of scared fowl. It ended with a tumble of a row of milk-pans toward chaos, and the door flew open and Uncle Fly appeared.

"What on earth!" said my grandmother, starting up. "That you, 'Liakim? Why on earth *must* you come in the back way and knock down all my milk-pans?"

"Why, I came 'cross lots from Aunt Bathsheba Sawin's," said Uncle Fly, dancing in, "and I got caught in those pesky blackberry-bushes in the graveyard, and I do believe I've torn my breeches all to pieces," he added, pirouetting and frisking with very airy gyrations, and trying vainly to get a view of himself behind, in which operation he went round and round as a cat does after her tail.

"Laws a-massy, 'Liakim!" said my grandmother, whose ears were startled by a peculiar hissing sound in the sink-room, which caused her to spring actively in that direction. "Well, now, you have been and done it! You've gone and fidgeted the tap out of my beer-barrel, and here's the beer all over the floor. I hope you're satisfied now."

"Sorry for it. Didn't mean to. I'll wipe it right up. Where's a towel, or floor-cloth, or something?" cried Uncle Fly, whirling in more active circles round and round, till he seemed to me to have a dozen pairs of legs.

"Do sit down, 'Liakim," said my grandmother. "Of course you didn't mean to; but next time don't come bustling and whirligging through my back sink-room after dark. I do believe you never will be quiet till you're in your grave."

"Sit down, uncle," said Bill. "Never mind mother, — she'll come all right by and by. And never mind your breeches, — all things earthly are transitory, as Parson Lothrop told us to-day. Now let's come back to our Sunday talk. Did ever anybody see such an astonishing providence as Miss Mehitable Rossiter's bonnet to-day?

Does it belong to the old or the new dispensation, do you think?"

"Bill, I'm astonished at you!" said Aunt Lois.

"Miss Mehitable is of a most respectable family," said Aunt Keziah, reprovingly. "Her father and grandfather and great-grandfather were all ministers; and two of her mother's brothers, Jeduthun and Amariah."

"Now, take care, youngster," said Uncle Fly. "You see you young colts mustn't be too airy. When a fellow begins to speak evil of bonnets, nobody knows where he may end."

"Bless me, one and all of you," said Bill, "I have the greatest respect for Miss Mehitable. Furthermore, I like her. She's a real spicy old concern. I'd rather talk with her than any dozen of modern girls. But I do wish she'd give me that bonnet to put in our Cambridge cabinet. I'd tell 'em it was the wing of a Madagascar bat. Blessed old soul, how innocent she sat under it! — never knowing to what wandering thoughts it was giving rise. Such bonnets interfere with my spiritual progress."

At this moment, by the luck that always brings in the person people are talking of, Miss Mehitable came in, with the identical old wonder on her head. Now, outside of our own blood-relations, no one that came within our doors ever received a warmer welcome than Miss Mehitable. Even the children loved her, with that instinctive sense by which children and dogs learn the discerning of spirits. To be sure she was as gaunt and brown as the Ancient Mariner, but hers was a style of ugliness that was neither repulsive nor vulgar. Personal uncomeliness has its differing characters, and there are some very homely women who have a style that amounts to something like beauty. I know that this is not the common view of the matter; but I am firm in the faith that some very homely women have a certain attraction about them which is increased by their homeliness. It is like the quaintness of Japanese china, — not beautiful, but having a strong, pronounced character, as far remote as possible from the ordinary and vulgar, and which, in union with vigorous and agreeable traits of mind, is more stimulating than any mere insipid beauty.

In short, Miss Mehitable was a specimen of what I should call the good-goblin style of beauty. And people liked her so much that they came to like the singularities which individualized her from all other people. Her features were prominent and harsh; her eyebrows were shaggy, and finished abruptly half across her brow, leaving but half an eyebrow on each side. She had, however, clear, trustworthy, steady eyes, of a greenish gray, which impressed one with much of that idea of steadfast faithfulness that one sees in the eyes of some good, homely dogs. "Faithful and true," was written in her face as legibly as eyes could write it.

For the rest, Miss Mehitable had a strong mind, was an omnivorous reader, apt, ready in conversation, and with a droll, original way of viewing things, which made her society ever stimulating. To me her house was always full of delightful images, — a great, calm, cool, shady, old-fashioned house, full of books and of quaint old furniture, with a garden on one side where were no end of lilies, hollyhocks, pinks, and peonies, to say nothing of currants, raspberries, apples, and pears, and other carnal delights, all of which good Miss Mehitable was free to dispense to her child-visitors. It was my image of heaven to be allowed to go to spend an afternoon with Miss Mehitable, and establish myself, in a shady corner of the old study which contained her father's library, over an edition of Aesop's Fables illustrated with plates, which, opened, was an endless field of enchantment to me.

Miss Mehitable lived under the watch and charge of an ancient female domestic named Polly Shubel. Polly was a representative specimen of the now extinct species of Yankee serving-maids. She had been bred up from a child in the Rossiter family of some generations back. She was of that peculiar kind of constitution, known in New England, which merely becomes drier and tougher with the advance of time, without giving any other indications of old age. The exact number of her years was a point unsettled even among the most skilful genealogists of Oldtown. Polly was a driving, thrifty, doctrinal and practical female, with strong bones and muscles, and strong opinions, believing most potently in early rising, soap and sand, and the Assembly's Catechism, and knowing *certainly* all that she did know. Polly considered Miss Mehitable as a sort of child under her wardship, and conducted the whole business of life for her with a sovereign and unanswerable authority. As Miss Mehitable's tastes were in the world of books and

ideas, rather than of physical matters, she resigned herself to Polly's sway with as good a grace as possible,
though sometimes she felt that it rather abridged her
freedom of action.

Luckily for my own individual self, Polly patronized
me, and gave me many a piece of good advice,
sweetened with gingerbread, when I went to visit Miss
Rossiter. I counted Miss Mehitable among my personal
friends; so to-night, when she came in, I came quickly
and laid hold of the skirt of her gown, and looked
admiringly upon her dusky face, under the portentous
shadow of a great bonnet shaded by nodding bows of
that preternatural color which people used to call olive-
green. She had a word for us all, a cordial grasp of the
hand for my mother, who sat silent and thoughtful in
her corner, and a warm hand-shake all round.

"You see," she said, drawing out an old-fashioned
snuff-box, and tapping upon it, "my house grew so
stupid that I must come and share my pinch of snuff
with you. It's windy out to-night, and I should think a
storm was brewing; and the rattling of one's own
window-blinds, as one sits alone, isn't half so amusing as
some other things."

"You know, Miss Rossiter, we're always delighted to
have you come in," said my grandmother, and my Aunt
Lois, and my Aunt Keziah, all at once. This, by the way,
was a little domestic trick that the females of our family
had; and, as their voices were upon very different keys,
the effect was somewhat peculiar. My Aunt Lois's voice
was high and sharp, my grandmother's a hearty chest-

tone, while Aunt Keziah's had an uncertain buzz between the two, like the vibration of a loose string; but as they all had corresponding looks and smiles of welcome, Miss Mehitable was pleased.

"I always indulge myself in thinking I am welcome," she said. "And now pray how is our young scholar, Master William Badger? What news do you bring us from old Harvard?"

"Almost anything you want to hear, Miss Mehitable. You know that I am your most devoted slave."

"Not so sure of that, sir," she said, with a whimsical twinkle of her eye. "Don't you know that your sex are always treacherous? How do I know that you don't serve up old Miss Rossiter when you give representations of the Oldtown curiosities there at Cambridge? We are a set here that might make a boy's fortune in that line, — now aren't we?"

"How do you know that I do serve up Oldtown curiosities?" said Bill, somewhat confused, and blushing to the roots of his hair.

"How do I know? Can the Ethiopian change his skin, or the leopard his spots? and can you help being a mimic, as you were born, always were and always will be?"

"O, but I'm sure, Miss Mehitable, Bill never would, — he has too much respect," said Aunt Keziah and Aunt Lois, simultaneously again.

"Perhaps not; but if he wants to, he's welcome. What are queer old women for, if young folks may not have a good laugh out of them now and then? If it's only a friendly laugh, it's just as good as crying, and better too. I'd like to be made to laugh at myself. I think generally we take ourselves altogether too seriously. What now, bright eyes?" she added, as I nestled nearer to her. "Do you want to come up into an old woman's lap? Well, here you come. Bless me, what a tangle of curls we have here! Don't your thoughts get caught in these curls sometimes?"

I looked bashful and wistful at this address, and Miss Mehitable went on twining my curls around her fingers, and trotting me on her knee, lulling me into a delicious dreaminess, in which she seemed to me to be one of those nice, odd-looking old fairy women that figure to such effect in stories.

The circle all rose again as Major Broad came in. Aunt Lois thought, with evident anguish, of the best room. Here was the Major, sure enough, and we all sitting round the kitchen fire! But my grandfather and grandmother welcomed him cheerfully to their corner, and enthroned him in my grandfather's splint-bottomed rocking-chair, where he sat far more comfortably than if he had been perched on a genteel, slippery-bottomed stuffed chair with claw feet.

The Major performed the neighborly kindnesses of the occasion in an easy way. He spoke a few words to my mother of the esteem and kindness he had felt for my father, in a manner that called up the blood into her thin cheeks, and made her eyes dewy with tears. Then he turned to the young collegian, recognizing him as one of the rising lights of Oldtown.

"Our only nobility now," he said to my grandfather. "We've cut off everything else: no distinction now, sir, but educated and uneducated."

"It is a hard struggle for our human nature to give up titles and ranks, though," said Miss Mehitable. "For my part, I have a ridiculous kindness for them yet. I know it's all nonsense; but I can't help looking back to the court we used to have at the Government House in Boston. You know it was something to hear of the goings and doings of my Lord this and my Lady that, and of Sir Thomas and Sir Charles, and all the rest of 'em."

"Yes," said Bill; "the Oldtown folks call their minister's wife Lady yet."

"Well, that's a little comfort," said Miss Mehitable; "one don't want life an entire dead level. Do let us have one titled lady among us."

"And a fine lady she is," said the Major. "Our parson did a good thing in that alliance."

While the conversation was thus taking a turn of the most approved genteel style, Aunt Keziah's ears heard alarming premonitory sounds outside the door. "Who's that at the scraper?" said she.

"O, it's Sam Lawson," said Aunt Lois, with a sort of groan. "You may be sure of that."

"Come in, Sam, my boy," said Uncle Bill, opening the door. "Glad to see you."

"Wal now, Mr. Badger," said Sam, with white eyes of veneration, "I'm real glad to see ye. I told Hepsy you'd want to see me. You're the fust one of my Saturday arternoon fishin' boys that's got into college, and I'm 'mazing proud on't. I tell you I walk tall, — ask 'em if I don't, round to the store.''

"You always were gifted in that line," said Bill. "But come, sit down in the corner and tell us what you've been about."

"Wal, you see, I thought I'd just go over to North Parish this arternoon, just for a change, like, and I wanted to hear one of them *Hopkintinsians* they tell so much about; and Parson Simpson, he's one on 'em.''

"You ought not to be roving off on Sunday, leaving your own meeting," said my grandfather.

"Wall, you see, Deacon Badger, I'm interested in these 'ere new doctrines. I met your Polly a goin' over, too," he said to Miss Mehitable.

"O yes," said Miss Mehitable, "Polly is a great Hopkinsian. She can hardly have patience to sit under our Parson Lothrop's preaching. It's rather hard on me, because Polly makes it a point of conscience to fight every one of his discourses over to me in my parlor. Somebody gave Polly an Arminian tract last Sunday, entitled, 'The Apostle Paul an Arminian.' It would have done you good to hear Polly's comments. ' 'Postle Paul an Arminian! He's the biggest 'lectioner of 'em all.' ''

"That he is," said my grandmother, warmly. "Polly's read her Bible to some purpose."

"Well, Sam, what did you think of the sermon?" said Uncle Bill.

"Wal," said Sam, leaning over the fire, with his long, bony hands alternately raised to catch the warmth, and then dropped with an utter laxness, when the warmth became too pronounced, "Parson Simpson's a smart man; but, I tell ye, it's kind o' discouragin! Why, he said our state and condition by nature was just like this. We was clear down in a well fifty feet deep, and the sides all round nothin' but glare ice; but we was under immediate obligations to get out, 'cause we was free, voluntary agents. But nobody ever had got out, and nobody would, unless the Lord reached down and took 'em. And whether he would or not nobody could tell; it was all sovereignty. He said there wa'n't one in a hundred, — not one in a thousand, — not one in ten thousand, — that would be saved. Lordy massy, says I to myself, ef that's so they're any of 'em welcome to my chance. And so I kind o' ris up and come out, 'cause I'd got a pretty long walk home, and I wanted to go round by South Pond, and inquire about Aunt Sally Morse's toothache."

"I heard the whole sermon over from Polly," said Miss Mehitable, "and as it was not a particularly cheerful subject to think of, I came over here." These words were said with a sort of chilly, dreary sigh, that made me turn and look up in Miss Mehitable's face. It looked haggard and weary, as of one tired of struggling with painful thoughts.

"Wal," said Sam Lawson, "I stopped a minute round to your back door, Miss Rossiter, to talk with Polly about the sermon. I was a tellin' Polly that that 'ere was puttin' inability a leetle too strong."

"Not a bit, not a bit," said Uncle Fly, "so long as it's moral inability. That's the point, ye see, — *moral*, — that's the word. That makes it all right."

"Wal," said Sam, "I was a puttin' it to Polly this way. Ef a man's cut off his hands, it ain't right to require him to chop wood. Wal, Polly, she says he'd no business to cut his hands off; and so he ought to be required to chop the wood all the same. Wal, I told her it was Adam chopped our hands off. But she said, no; it was we did it *in* Adam, and she brought up the catechise plain enough, — *We sinned in him,* and fell with him.'"

"She had you there, Sam," said Uncle Fly, with great content. "You won't catch Polly tripping on the catechism."

"Well, for my part," said Major Broad, "I don't like these doctrinal subtilties, Deacon Badger. Now I've got a volume of Mr. Addison's religious writings that seem to me about the right thing. They're very pleasing reading. Mr. Addison is my favourite author of a Sunday."

"I'm afraid Mr. Addison had nothing but just mere morality and natural religion," said my grandmother, who could not be withheld from bearing her testimony. "You don't find any of the discriminating doctrines in Mr. Addison. Major Broad, did you ever read Mr. Bellamy's 'True Religion Delineated and Distinguished from all Counterfeits'?"

"No, madam, I never did," said Major Broad.

"Well, I earnestly hope you will read *that* book," said my grandmother.

"My wife is always at me about one good book or another," said my grandfather; "but I manage to do with my old Bible. I haven't used that up yet."

"I should know about Dr. Bellamy's book by this

time," said Miss Mehitable, "for Polly intrenches herself in that, and preaches out of it daily. Polly certainly missed her vocation when she was trained for a servant. She is a born professor of theology. She is so circumstantial about all that took place at the time the angels fell, and when the covenant was made with Adam in the Garden of Eden, that I sometimes question whether she really might not have been there personally. Polly is particularly strong on Divine sovereignty. She thinks it applies to everything under the sun except my affairs. Those she chooses to look after herself."

"Well," said Major Broad, "I am not much of a theologian. I want to be taught my duty. Parson Lothrop's discourses are generally very clear and practical, and they suit me."

"They are good as far as they go," said my grandmother; "but I like good, strong, old-fashioned doctrine. I like such writers as Mr. Edwards and Dr. Bellamy and Dr. Hopkins. It's all very well, your essays on cheerfulness and resignation, and all that; but I want something that takes strong hold of you, so that you feel something has got you that *can* hold."

"The Cambridge Platform, for instance," said Uncle Bill.

"Yes, my son, the Cambridge Platform. I ain't ashamed of it. It was made by men whose shoe-latchet we aren't worthy to unloose. I believe it, — every word on't. I believe it, and I'm going to believe it."

"And would if there was twice as much of it," said Uncle Bill. "That's right, mother, stand up for your colors. I admire your spirit. But, Sam, what does Hepsy think of all this? I suppose you enlighten her when you return from your investigations."

"Wal, I try to. But lordy massy, Mr. Badger, Hepsy don't take no kind o' interest in the doctrines, no more 'n nothin' at all. She's so kind o' worldly, Hepsy is. It's allers meat and drink, meat and drink, with her. That's all she's thinkin' of."

"And if *you* would think more of such things, she wouldn't have to think so much," said Aunt Lois, sharply. "Don't you know the Bible says, that the man that provideth not for his own household hath denied the faith, and is worse than an infidel?"

"I don't see," said Sam, slowly flopping his great hands up and down over the blaze, — "I railly don't see why folks are allers a throwin' up that 'ere text at me. I'm sure I work as hard as a man ken. Why, I was a workin' last night till nigh twelve o'clock, doin' up odd jobs o' blacksmithin'. They kind o' 'cumulate, ye know."

"Mr. Lawson," said my grandmother, with a look of long-suffering patience, "how often and often must I tell you, that if you'd be steadier round your home, and work in regular hours, Hepsy would be more comfortable, and things would go on better?"

"Lordy massy, Mis' Badger, bless your soul and body, ye don't know nothin' about it; — ye don't know nothin' what I undergo. Hepsy, she's at me from morning till night. First it's one thing, and then another. One day it rains, and her clothes-line breaks. She's at me 'bout that. Now I tell her, 'Hepsy, I ain't to blame, — I don't make the rain.' And then another day she's at me agin cause the wind's east, and fetches the smoke down chimbley. I tell her, 'Hepsy, now look here, — *do* I make the wind blow?' But it's no use talkin' to Hepsy."

"Well, Sam, I take your part," said Bill. "I always knew you was a regular martyr. Come, boys, go down cellar and draw a pitcher of cider. We'll stay him with flagons, and comfort him with apples. Won't we, Sam?"

As Sam was prime favorite with all boys, my brother Bill and I started willingly enough on this errand, one carrying the candle and the other a great stone pitcher of bountiful proportions, which always did hospitable duty on similar occasions.

Just as we returned, bearing our pitcher, there came another rap at the outside door of the kitchen, and Old Betty Poganut and Sally Wonsamug stood at the door.

"Well, now, Mis' Badger," said Betty, "Sally and me, we thought we must jest run in, we got so scar't. We was coming through that Bill Morse's woods, and there come such a flash o' lightnin' it most blinded us, and the wind blew enough to blow a body over; and we thought there was a storm right on us, and we run jest as fast as we could. We didn't know what to do, we was so scar't. I'm mortal 'fraid of lightning."

"Why, Betty, you forgot the sermon to-day. You should have said your prayers, as Parson Lothrop tells you," said my grandfather.

"Well, I did kind o' put up a sort o' silent 'jaculation, as a body may say. That is, I jest said, 'O Lord,' and kind o' gin him a wink, you know."

"O, you did?" said my grandfather.

"Yes, I kind o' thought He'd know what I meant."

My grandfather turned with a smile to Miss Mehitable. "These Indians have their own wild ways of looking at things, after all."

"Well, now, I s'pose you haven't had a bit of supper, either of you," said my grandmother, getting up. "It's commonly the way of it."

"Well, to tell the truth, I was sayin' to Sarah that if we come down to Mis' Deacon Badger's I shouldn't wonder if we got something good," said Betty, her broad, coarse face and baggy cheeks beginning to be illuminated with a smile.

"Here, Horace, you come and hold the candle while I go into the buttery and get 'em some cold pork and beans," said my grandmother, cheerily. "The poor creturs don't get a good meal of victuals very often; and I baked a good lot on purpose."

If John Bunyan had known my grandmother, he certainly would have introduced her in some of his histories as "the housekeeper whose name was Bountiful"; and under her care an ample meal of brown bread and pork and beans was soon set forth on the table in the corner of the kitchen, to which the two hungry Indian women sat down with the appetite of wolves. A large mug was placed between them, which Uncle Bill filled to the brim with cider.

"I s'pose you'd like twice a mug better than once a mug, Sally," he said, punning on her name.

"O, if the mug's only big enough," said Sally, her snaky eyes gleaming with appetite; "and it's always a good big mug one gets here."

Sam Lawson's great white eyes began irresistibly to

wander in the direction of the plentiful cheer which was being so liberally dispensed at the other side of the room.

"Want some, Sam, my boy?" said Uncle Bill, with a patronizing freedom.

"Why, bless your soul, Master Bill, I wouldn't care a bit if I took a plate o' them beans and some o' that 'ere pork. Hepsy didn't save no beans for me; and, walkin' all the way from North Parish, I felt kind o' empty and windy, as a body may say. You know Scriptur' tells about bein' filled with the east wind; but I never found it noways satisfyin', – it sets sort o' cold on the stomach."

"Draw up, Sam, and help yourself," said Uncle Bill, putting plate and knife and fork before him; and Sam soon showed that he had a vast internal capacity for the stowing away of beans and brown bread.

Meanwhile Major Broad and my grandfather drew their chairs together, and began a warm discussion of the Constitution of the United States, which had been recently presented for acceptance in a Convention of the State of Massachusetts.

"I haven't seen you, Major Broad," said my grandfather, "since you came back from the Convention. I'm very anxious to have our State of Massachusetts accept that Constitution. We're in an unsettled condition now; we don't know fairly where we are. If we accept this Constitution, we shall be a nation, – we shall have something to go to work on."

"Well, Deacon Badger, to say the truth, I could not

vote for this Constitution in Convention. They have adopted it by a small majority; but I shall be bound to record my dissent from it."

"Pray, Major, what are your objections?" said Miss Mehitable.

"I have two. One is, it gives too much power to the President. There's an appointing power and a power of patronage that will play the mischief some day in the hands of an ambitious man. That's one objection. The other is the recognizing and encouraging of slavery in the Constitution. That is such a dreadful wrong, — such a shameful inconsistency, — when we have just come through a battle for the doctrine that all men are free and equal, to turn round and found our national government on a recognition of African slavery. It cannot and will not come to good."

"O, well," said my grandfather, "slavery will gradually die out. You see how it is going in the New England States."

"I cannot think so," said the Major. "I have a sort of feeling about this that I cannot resist. If we join those States that still mean to import and use slaves, our nation will meet some dreadful punishment. I am certain of it."*

"Well, really," said my grandfather, "I'm concerned to hear you speak so. I have felt such anxiety to have

* The dissent of Major Broad of Natick, and several others, on the grounds above stated, may still be read in the report of the proceedings of the Convention that ratified the Constitution. [Stowe's note]

something settled. You see, without a union we are all afloat, — we are separate logs, but no raft."

"Yes," said Miss Mehitable, "but nothing can be settled that isn't founded on right. We ought to dig deep, and lay our foundation on a rock, when we build for posterity."

"Were there many of your way of thinking in the Convention, Major?" said my grandfather.

"Well, we had a pretty warm discussion, and we came very near to carrying it. Now, in Middlesex County, for instance, where we are, there were only seventeen in favor of the Constitution, and twenty-five against; and in Worcester County there were only seven in favour and forty-three against. Well, they carried it at last by a majority of nineteen; but the minority recorded their protest. Judge Widgery of Portland, General Thompson of Topsham, and Dr. Taylor of Worcester, rather headed the opposition. Then the town of Andover instructed its representative, Mr. Symmes, to vote against it, but he didn't, he voted on the other side, and I understand they are dreadfully indignant about it. I saw a man from Andover last week who said that he actually thought Symmes would be obliged to leave the town, he was so dreadfully unpopular."

"Well, Major Broad, I agree with you," said my grandmother, heartily, "and I honor you for the stand you took. Slavery is a sin and a shame; and I say, with Jacob, 'O my soul, come not thou into their secret, — unto their assembly, mine honor, be not thou united.' I wish we may keep clear on't. I don't want anything that we can't ask God's blessing on heartily, and we certainly can't on this. Why, anybody that sees that great scar on Caesar's forehead sees what slavery comes to."

My grandmother always pointed her anti-slavery arguments with an appeal to this mark of ill-usage which old Caesar had received at the hands of a brutal master years before, and the appeal never failed to convince the domestic circle.

"Well," said my grandfather, after some moments of silence, in which he sat gazing fixedly at the great red coals of a hickory log, "you see, Major, it's done, and can't be helped."

"It's done," said the Major, "but in my opinion mischief will come of it as sure as there is a God in heaven."

"Let's hope not," said my grandfather, placidly.

Outside the weather was windy and foul, the wind rattling doors, shaking and rumbling down the chimney, and causing the great glowing circle lighted by the fire to seem warmer and brighter. The Indian women and Sam Lawson, having finished their meal and thoroughly cleaned out the dishes, grouped themselves about the end of the ingle already occupied by black Caesar, and began a little private gossip among themselves.

"I say," says Sam, raising his voice to call my grandfather's attention, "do you know, Deacon Badger, whether anybody is living in the Dench house now?"

"There wasn't, the last I knew about it," said my grandfather.

"Wal, you won't make some folks believe but what that 'ere house is haunted."

"Haunted!" said Miss Mehitable; "nothing more likely. What old house isn't? — if one only knew it; and that certainly ought to be if ever a house was."

"But this 'ere's a regular *haunt*," said Sam. "I was a talkin' the other night with Bill Payne and Jake Marshall, and they both on 'em said that they'd seen strange things in them grounds, — they'd seen a figger of a man —"

"With his head under his arm," suggested Uncle Bill.

"No, a man in a long red cloak," said Sam Lawson, "such as Sir Harry Frankland used to wear."

"Poor Sir Harry!" said Miss Mehitable, "has he come to that?"

"Did you know Sir Harry?" said Aunt Lois.

"I have met him once or twice at the Governor's house," said Miss Mehitable. "Lady Lothrop knew Lady Frankland very well."

"Well, Sam," said Uncle Bill, "do let's hear the end of this haunting."

"Nothin', only the other night I was a goin' over to watch with Lem Moss, and I passed pretty nigh the Dench place, and I thought I'd jest look round it a spell. And as sure as you're alive I see smoke a comin' out of the chimbley."

"I didn't know as ghosts ever used the fireplaces," said Uncle Bill. "Well, Sam, did you go in?"

"No, I was pretty much in a hurry; but I told Jake and Bill, and then they each on 'em had something to match that they'd seen. As nigh as I can make it out, there's that 'ere boy that they say was murdered and thrown down that 'ere old well walks sometimes. And then there's a woman appears to some, and this 'ere man in a red cloak; and they think it's Sir Harry in his red cloak."

"For my part," said Aunt Lois, "I never had much opinion of Sir Harry Frankland, or Lady Frankland either. I don't think such goings on ever ought to be countenanced in society."

"They both repented bitterly, — repented in sackcloth and ashes," said Miss Mehitable. "And if God forgives such sins, why shouldn't we?"

"What was the story?" said Major Broad.

"Why," said Aunt Lois, "haven't you heard of Agnes Surradge, of Marblehead? She was housemaid in a tavern there, and Sir Harry fell in love with her, and took her and educated her. That was well enough; but when she'd done going to school he took her home to his house in Boston, and called her his daughter; although people became pretty sure that the connection was not what it should be, and they refused to have anything to do with her. So he bought this splendid place out in the woods, and built a great palace of a house, and took Miss Agnes out there. People that wanted to be splendidly entertained, and that were not particular as to morals, used to go out to visit them."

"I used to hear great stories of their wealth and pomp and luxury," said my grandmother, "but I mourned over it, that it should come to this in New England, that people could openly set such an example and be tolerated. It wouldn't have been borne a generation before, I can tell you. No, indeed, — the magistrates would have put a stop to it. But these noblemen, when they came over to America, seemed to think themselves lords of God's heritage, and free to do just as they pleased."

"But," said Miss Mehitable, "they repented, as I said. He took her to England, and there his friends refused to receive her; and then he was appointed Ambassador to Lisbon, and he took her there. On the day of the great earthquake Sir Harry was riding with a lady of the court when the shock came, and in a moment, without warning, they found themselves buried under the ruins of a building they were passing. He wore a scarlet cloak, as was the fashion; and they say that in her dying agonies the poor creature bit through this cloak and sleeve into the flesh of his arm, and made a mark that he carried to his dying day. Sir Harry was saved by Agnes Surradge. She came over the ruins, calling and looking for him, and he heard her voice and answered, and she got men to come and dig him out. When he was in that dreadful situation, he made a vow to God, if He would save his life, that he would be a different man. And he was a changed man from that day. He was married to Agnes Surradge as soon as they could get a priest to perform the ceremony; and when he took her back to England all his relations received her, and she was presented in court and moved in society with perfect acceptance."

"I don't think it ever ought to have been," said Aunt Lois. "Such women never ought to be received."

"What! is there no place of repentance for a woman?" said Miss Mehitable. "Christ said, 'Neither do I condemn thee; go and sin no more.'"

I noticed again that sort of shiver of feeling in Miss Mehitable; and there was a peculiar thrill in her voice, as she said these words, that made me sensible that she was speaking from some inward depth of feeling.

"Don't you be so hard and sharp, Lois," said my grandmother; "sinners must have patience with sinners."

"Especially with sinners of quality, Lois," said Uncle Bill. "By all accounts Sir Harry and Lady Frankland swept all before them when they came back to Boston."

"Of course," said Miss Mehitable; "what was done in court would be done in Boston, and whom Queen Charlotte received would be received in our upper circles. Lady Lothrop never called on her till she was Lady Frankland, but after that I believe she was visited out at their place."

"Wal, I've heerd 'em say," said Sam Lawson, "that it would take a woman two days jest to get through cleaning the silver that there was in that 'ere house, to say nothing about the carpets and the curtains and the tapestry. But then, when the war broke out, Lady Frankland, she took most of it back to England, I guess, and the house has been back and forward to one and another. I never could rightly know jest who did live in it. I heard about some French folks that lived there one time. I thought some day, when I hadn't nothin' else to do, I'd jest walk over to old Granny Walker's that lives over the other side of Hopkinton. She used to be a housekeeper to Lady Frankland, and I could get particulars out o' her."

"Well," said Miss Mehitable, "I know one woman that

must go back to a haunted house, and that is this present one." So saying, she rose and put me off her knee.

"Send this little man over to see me to-morrow," she said to my mother. "Polly has a cake for him, and I shall find something to amuse him."

Major Broad, with old-fashioned gallantry, insisted on waiting on Miss Mehitable home; and Sam Lawson reluctantly tore himself from the warm corner to encounter the asperities of his own fireside.

"Here, Sam," said good-natured Bill, — "here's a great red apple for Hepsy."

"Ef I dares to go nigh enough to give it to her," said Sam, with a grimace. "She's allers a castin' it up at me that I don't want to set with her at home. But lordy massy, she don't consider that a fellow don't want to set and be hectored and lectured when he can do better elsewhere."

"True enough, Sam; but give my regards to her."

As to the two Indian women, they gave it as their intention to pass the night by the kitchen fire; and my grandmother, to whom such proceedings were not at all strange, assented, — producing for each a blanket, which had often seen similar service. My grandfather closed the evening by bringing out his great Bible and reading a chapter. Then we all knelt down in prayer.

So passed an evening in my grandmother's kitchen, — where religion, theology, politics, the gossip of the day, and the legends of the supernatural all conspired to weave a fabric of thought quaint and various. Intense earnestness, a solemn undertone of deep mournful awe, was overlaid with quaint traceries of humor, strange and weird in their effect. I was one of those children who are all ear, — dreamy listeners, who brood over all that they hear, without daring to speak of it; and in this evening's conversation I had heard enough to keep my eyes broad open long after my mother had laid me in bed. The haunted house and its vague wonders filled my mind, and I determined to question Sam Lawson yet more about it.

But now that I have fairly introduced myself, the scene of my story, and many of the actors in it, I must take my reader off for a while, and relate a history that must at last blend with mine in one story.

12. THE NIGHT-WATCHERS

from *The Little Minister* [Chapt. III]
by James M. Barrie, 1891

Sir James Barrie is known as the creator of Peter Pan, the author of such fine plays of ironic social comment as The Admirable Crichton *and* Dear Brutus, *and the writer of a number of once-popular romances. Best known of this last group is* The Little Minister, *which enjoyed much success when it was published as a novel in 1891, and even more success when it was produced as a play in 1897, with Maude Adams as the star.*

Few would argue that the story's main appeal is not the highly romantic, even sentimental, love story of the young minister, Gavin Dishart, and the "Egyptian," Babby; yet woven through the tale is much of that attention to religious matters which indicates how naturally in 1891 an author could expect from his readers knowledge of and interest in religion. Just as American audiences of a generation earlier had read books like Oldtown Folks *with interest, so British and American audiences of the late years of the century were glad to find in a book like* The Little Minister *much discussion of the education and proper role of a clergyman. Barrie's story shows, indeed, that in Scotland young men who managed to prepare themselves for the ministry, overcoming poverty and even privation to do so, were viewed almost as heroes.*

For the twentieth-century reader it may come as a surprise to learn that the fervid religious arguments in this chapter are not between believers and atheists (except one!) or Christians and non-Christians, or Protestants and Catholics — but are all within the "family" of Presbyterians. Since shades of religious belief were to Scots, from the days of John Knox almost to the present, matters of first importance, the Presbyterianism which in 1592 became the Established Church of Scotland tended to sliver into sects and sub-sects under the pressure of changing times and attitudes. The Auld Licht (Old Light) Church which Gavin serves is a very conservative group which for a time broke entirely away from the Established Church (only to be re-united with it in the twentieth century). Taking part in the discussion in this chapter are members of Gavin's Auld Licht Church, an atheist, a member of the Established Church (of which Mr. Duthie is minister), and a member of the United Presbyterian Church ("U.P.") — the most progressive group in the Scotland of Gavin's day. The arguments regarding the "Paraphrases" have to do with the reluctance of the

*Church of Scotland, like other Calvinist churches, to
allow anything except the Psalms to be sung in church.
In the late eighteenth century the Church of Scotland
had cautiously approved paraphrases of other scriptural
passages, but a century later the more conservative Scots
were still resisting such daring. The Feargus O'Connor
whom the atheist would prefer to hear quoted, rather
than Scripture, was a radical leader of the Chartists, that
group of reformers which sought a "People's Charter"
guaranteeing improved living conditions and civil rights
for working people.*

*In the chapter given here twenty-one-year-old Gavin
Dishart and his mother arrive in "Thrums" where Gavin
is to be the new "Auld Licht" minister. Even the hard-
working weavers, harried by new threats of reductions
in their miserable earnings, find time to discuss the new
minister, and to watch every move he makes. These
moves indicate that Gavin is both a true minister and a
true twenty-one-year-old.*

What first struck Margaret in Thrums was the smell of
caddis. The town smells of caddis no longer, but whiffs
of it may be got even now as one passes the houses of
the old, where the lay still swings at little windows like a
great ghost pendulum. To me it is a homely smell, which

I draw in with a great breath, but it was as strange to Margaret as the weavers themselves, who, in their coloured nightcaps and corduroys streaked with threads, gazed at her and Gavin. The little minister was trying to look severe and old, but twenty-one was in his eye.

"Look, mother, at that white house with the green roof. That is the manse."

The manse stands high, with a sharp eye on all the town. Every back window in the Tenements has a glint of it, and so the back of the Tenements is always better behaved than the front. It was in the front that Jamie Don, a pitiful bachelor all his life because he thought the women proposed, kept his ferrets, and here, too, Beattie hanged himself, going straight to the clothes-posts for another rope when the first one broke, such was his determination. In the front Sanders Gilruth openly boasted (on Don's potato-pit) that by having a seat in two churches he could lie in bed on Sabbath and get the credit of being at one or other. (Gavin made short work of him.) To the right-minded the Auld Licht manse was as a family Bible, ever lying open before them, but Beattie spoke for more than himself when he said, "Dagone that manse! I never gie a swear but there it is glowering at me."

The manse looks down on the town from the north-east, and is reached from the road that leaves Thrums behind it in another moment by a wide, straight path, so rough that to carry a fraught of water to the manse without spilling was to be superlatively good at one thing. Packages in a cart it set leaping like trout in a fishing-creel. Opposite the opening of the garden wall in the manse, where for many years there had been an intention of putting up a gate, were two big stones a yard apart, standing ready for the winter, when the path was often a rush of yellow water, and this the only bridge to the glebe dyke, down which the minister walked to church.

When Margaret entered the manse on Gavin's arm, it was a whitewashed house of five rooms, with a garret in which the minister could sleep if he had guests, as during the Fast week. It stood with its garden within high walls, and the roof facing southward was carpeted with moss that shone in the sun a dozen shades of green and yellow. Three firs guarded the house from west winds, but blasts from the north often tore down the steep fields and skirled through the manse, banging all its doors at once. A beech, growing on the east side, leant over the roof as if to gossip with the well in the courtyard. The garden was to the south, and was over-full of gooseberry and currant bushes. It contained a summer seat where strange things were soon to happen.

Margaret would not even take off her bonnet until she had seen through the manse and opened all the presses. The parlour and kitchen were downstairs, and of the three rooms above, the study was so small that Gavin's predecessor could touch each of its walls without shifting his position. Every room save Margaret's had long-lidded beds, which close as if with shutters, but hers was coff-fronted, or comparatively open, with carving on the wood like the ornamentation of coffins. Where there were children in a house they liked to slope the boards of the closed-in bed against the dresser, and play at sliding down mountains on them.

But for many years there had been no children in the manse. He in whose ways Gavin was to attempt the heavy task of walking had been a widower three months after his marriage, a man narrow when he came to Thrums, but so large-hearted when he left that I, who know there is good in all the world because of the lovable souls I have met in this corner of it, yet cannot hope that many are as near to God as he. The most gladsome thing in the world is that few of us fall very low; the saddest that, with such capabilities, we seldom rise high. Of those who stand perceptibly above their fellows I have known very few; only Mr. Carfrae and two or three women.

Gavin only saw a very frail old minister who shook as he walked, as if his feet were striking against stones. He was to depart on the morrow to the place of his birth, but he came to the manse to wish his successor God-speed. Strangers were so formidable to Margaret that she only saw him from her window.

"May you never lose sight of God, Mr. Dishart," the old man said in the parlour. Then he added, as if he had asked too much: "May you never turn from Him as I often did when I was a lad like you."

As this aged minister, with the beautiful face that God gives to all who love Him and follow His commandments, spoke of his youth, he looked wistfully round the faded parlour.

"It is like a dream," he said. "The first time I entered this room the thought passed through me that I would cut down that cherry-tree because it kept out the light, but, you see, it outlives me. I grew old while looking for the axe. Only yesterday I was the young minister, Mr. Dishart, and to-morrow you will be the old one, bidding good-bye to your successor."

His eyes came back to Gavin's eager face.

"You are very young, Mr. Dishart?"

"Nearly twenty-one."

"Twenty-one! Ah, my dear sir, you do not know how pathetic that sounds to me. Twenty-one! We are children for the second time at twenty-one, and again when we are gray and put all our burden on the Lord. The young talk generously of relieving the old of their burdens, but the anxious heart is to the old when they see a load on the back of the young. Let me tell you, Mr. Dishart, that I would condone many things in one and twenty now that I dealt hardly with at middle age. God Himself, I think, is very willing to give one and twenty a second chance."

"I am afraid," Gavin said, anxiously, "that I look even younger."

"I think," Mr. Carfrae answered, smiling, "that your heart is as fresh as your face; and that is well. The useless men are those who never change with the years. Many views that I held to in my youth and long afterwards are a pain to me now, and I am carrying away from Thrums memories of errors into which I fell at every stage of my ministry. When you are older you will know that life is a long lesson in humility."

He paused.

"I hope," he said, nervously, "that you don't sing the Paraphrases?"

Mr. Carfrae had not grown out of all his prejudices, you see; indeed, if Gavin had been less bigoted than he on this question they might have parted stiffly. The old minister would rather have remained to die in his pulpit than surrender it to one who read his sermons. Others may blame him for this, but I must say here plainly that I never hear a minister reading without wishing to send him back to college.

"I cannot deny," Mr. Carfrae said, "that I broke down more than once today. This forenoon I was in Tillyloss, for the last time, and it so happens that there is scarcely a house in it in which I have not had a marriage or prayed over a coffin. Ah, sir, these are the scenes that make the minister more than all his sermons. You must join the family, Mr. Dishart, or you are only a minister once a week. And remember this, if your call is from above, it is a call to stay. Many such partings in a lifetime as I have had to-day would be too heart-rending."

"And yet," Gavin said, hesitatingly, "they told me in Glasgow that I had received a call from the mouth of hell."

"Those were cruel words, but they only mean that people who are seldom more than a day's work in advance of want sometimes rise in arms for food. Our weavers are passionately religious, and so independent that they dare any one to help them, but if their wages were lessened they could not live. And so at talk of reduction they catch fire. Change of any kind alarms them, and though they call themselves Whigs, they rose a few years ago over the paving of the streets and stoned the workmen, who were strangers, out of the town.

"And though you may have thought the place quiet to-day, Mr. Dishart, there was an ugly outbreak only two months ago, when the weavers turned on the manufacturers for reducing the price of the web, made a bonfire of some of their doors, and terrified one of them into leaving Thrums. Under the command of some Chartists, the people next paraded the streets to the music of fife and drum, and six policemen who drove up from Tilliedrum in a light cart were sent back tied to the seats."

"No one has been punished?"

"Not yet, but nearly two years ago there was a similar riot, and the sheriff took no action for months. Then one night the square suddenly filled with soldiers, and the ringleaders were seized in their beds. Mr. Dishart, the people are determined not to be caught in that way again, and ever since the rising a watch has been kept by night on every road that leads to Thrums. The signal that the soldiers are coming is to be the blowing of a horn. If you ever hear that horn, I implore you to hasten to the square."

"The weavers would not fight?"

"You do not know how the Chartists have fired this part of the country. One misty day, a week ago, I was on the hill; I thought I had it to myself, when suddenly I heard a voice cry sharply, 'Shoulder arms.' I could see no one, and after a moment I put it down to a freak of the wind. Then all at once the mist before me blackened, and a body of men seemed to grow out of it. They were not shadows; they were Thrums weavers drilling, with pikes in their hands.

"They broke up," Mr. Carfrae continued, after a pause, "at my entreaty, but they have met again since then."

"And there were Auld Lichts among them?" Gavin asked. "I should have thought they would be frightened at our precentor, Lang Tammas, who seems to watch for backsliding in the congregation as if he had pleasure in discovering it."

Gavin spoke with feeling, for the precentor had already put him through his catechism, and it was a stiff ordeal.

"The precentor!" said Mr. Carfrae. "Why, he was one of them."

The old minister, once so brave a figure, tottered as he rose to go, and reeled in a dizziness until he had walked a few paces. Gavin went with him to the foot of the manse road; without his hat, as all Thrums knew before bedtime.

"I begin," Gavin said, as they were parting, "where you leave off, and my prayer is that I may walk in your ways."

"Ah, Mr. Dishart," the white-haired minister said, with a sigh, "the world does not progress so quickly as a man grows old. You only begin where I began."

He left Gavin, and then, as if the little minister's last

words had hurt him, turned and solemnly pointed his staff upward. Such men are the strong nails that keep the world together.

The twenty-one-year-old minister returned to the manse somewhat sadly, but when he saw his mother at the window of her bedroom, his heart leapt at the thought that she was with him and he had eighty pounds a year. Gaily he waved both his hands to her, and she answered with a smile, and then, in his boyishness, he jumped over a gooseberry bush. Immediately afterwards he reddened and tried to look venerable, for while in the air he had caught sight of two women and a man watching him from the dyke. He walked severely to the door, and, again forgetting himself, was bounding up-stairs to Margaret, when Jean, the servant, stood scandalised in his way.

"I don't think she caught me," was Gavin's reflection, and "The Lord preserve's!" was Jean's.

Gavin found his mother wondering how one should set about getting a cup of tea in a house that had a servant in it. He boldly rang the bell, and the willing Jean answered it so promptly (in a rush and a jump) that Margaret was as much startled as Aladdin the first time he rubbed his lamp.

Manse servants of the most admired kind move softly, as if constant contact with a minister were goloshes to them; but Jean was new and raw, only having got her place because her father might be an elder any day. She had already conceived a romantic affection for her master; but to say "sir" to him — as she thirsted to do —

would have been as difficult to her as to swallow oysters. So anxious was she to please that when Gavin rang she fired herself at the bedroom, but bells were novelties to her as well as to Margaret, and she cried, excitedly, "What is 't?" thinking the house must be on fire.

"There's a curran folk at the back door," Jean announced later, "and their respects to you, and would you gie them some water out o' the well? It has been a drouth this aucht days, and the pumps is locked. Na," she said, as Gavin made a too liberal offer, "that would toom the well, and there's jimply enough for oursels. I should tell you, too, that three o' them is no Auld Lichts."

"Let that make no difference," Gavin said, grandly, but Jean changed his message to: "A bowlful apiece to Auld Lichts; all other denominations one cupful."

"Ay, ay," said Snecky Hobart, letting down the bucket, "and we'll include atheists among other denominations." The conversation came to Gavin and Margaret through the kitchen doorway.

"Dinna class Jo Cruickshanks wi' me," said Sam'l Langlands the U.P.

"Na, na," said Cruickshanks the atheist, "I'm ower independent to be religious. I dinna gang to the kirk to cry, 'Oh, Lord, gie, gie, gie.' "

"Take tent o' yoursel', my man," said Lang Tammas, sternly, "or you'll soon be whaur you would neifer [give] the warld for a cup o' that cauld water."

"Maybe you've ower keen an interest in the devil,

Tammas," retorted the atheist; "but, ony way, if it's heaven for climate, it's hell for company."

"Lads," said Snecky, sitting down on the bucket, "we'll send Mr. Dishart to Jo. He'll make another Rob Dow o' him."

"Speak mair reverently o' your minister," said the precentor. "He has the gift."

"I hinna naturally your solemn rasping word, Tammas, but in the heart I speak in all reverence. Lads, the minister has a word! I tell you he prays near like one giving orders."

"At first," Snecky continued, "I thocht yon lang candidate was the earnestest o' them a', and I dinna deny but when I saw him wi' his head bowed-like in prayer during the singing I says to mysel', 'Thou art the man.' Ay, but Betsy wraxed up her head, and he wasna praying. He was combing his hair wi' his fingers on the sly."

"You ken fine, Sneck," said Cruickshanks, "that you said 'Thou art the man' to ilka ane o' them, and just voted for Mr. Dishart because he preached hinmost."

"I didna say it to Mr. Urquhart, the ane that preached second," Sneck said. "That was the lad that gaed through ither [went pell mell]."

"Ay," said Susy Tibbits, nicknamed by Haggart "the Timidest Woman," because she once said she was too young to marry, "but I was fell sorry for him, just being overanxious. He began bonny, flinging himself, like ane inspired, at the pulpit door, but after Hendry Munn pointed at it, and cried out, 'Be cautious, the sneck's loose, 'he a' gaed to bits. What a coolness Hendry has, though I suppose it was his duty, him being kirk officer."

"We didna want a man," Lang Tammas said, "that could be put out by sic a sma' thing as that. Mr. Urquhart was in sic a ravel after it that when he gies out the first line o' the hunder and nineteenth psalm for singing, says he, 'and so on to the end.' Ay, that finished his chance."

"The noblest o' them to look at," said Tibbie Birse, "was that ane frae Aberdeen, him that had sic a saft side to Jacob."

"Ay," said Snecky, "and I speired at [asked] Doctor McQueen if I should vote for him. 'Looks like a genius, does he?' says the Doctor. 'Well, then,' says he, 'dinna vote for him, for my experience is that there's no folk sic idiots as them that looks like geniuses.' "

"Sal," Susy said, "It's a guid thing we've settled, for I enjoyed sitting like a judge upon them so muckle that I sair doubt it was a kind o' sport to me."

"It was no sport to them, Susy, I'se uphaud, but it is a blessing we've settled, and ondoubtedly we've got the pick o' them. The only thing Mr. Dishart did that made me oneasy was his saying the word Caesar as if it began wi' a *k*."

"He'll startle you mair afore you're done wi' him," the atheist said, maliciously. "I ken the ways o' thae ministers preaching for kirks. Oh, they're cunning. You was a' pleased that Mr. Dishart spoke about looms and webs, but, lathies, it was a trick. Ilka ane o' thae young

ministers has a sermon about looms for weaving con-
gregations, and a second about beating swords into
ploughshares for country places, and another on the
great catch of fishes for fishing villages. That's their
stock in trade; and just you wait and see if you dinna
get the ploughshares and the fishes afore the month's
out. A minister preaching for a kirk is one thing, but a
minister placed in't may be a very different berry."

"Joseph   Cruickshanks,"   cried   the   precentor,
passionately, "none o' your d—d blassphemy!"

They all looked at Whamond, and he dug his teeth
into his lips in shame.

"Wha's swearing now?" said the atheist.

But Whamond was quick.

"Matthew, twelve and thirty-one," he said.

"Dagont, Tammas," exclaimed the baffled Cruickshanks, "you're aye quoting Scripture. How do you no
quote Feargus O'Connor?"

"Lads," said Snecky, "Jo hasna heard Mr. Dishart's
sermons. Ay, we get it scalding when he comes to the
sermon. I canna thole a minister that preaches as if
heaven was round the corner."

"If you're hitting at our minister, Snecky," said
James Cochrane, "let me tell you he's a better man than
yours."

"A better curler, I dare say."

"A better prayer."

"Ay, he can pray for a black frost as if it was ane o'
the Royal Family. I ken his prayers, 'O Lord, let it haud
for anither day, and keep the snaw awa'.' Will you

pretend, Jeames, that Mr. Duthie could make onything o' Rob Dow?"

"I admit that Rob's awakening was an extraordinary thing, and sufficient to gie Mr. Dishart a name. But Mr. Carfrae was baffled wi' Rob, too."

"Jeames, if you had been in our kirk that day Mr. Dishart preached for't you would be wearying the now for Sabbath, to be back in't again. As you ken, that wicked man there, Jo Cruickshanks, got Rob Dow, drucken, cursing, poaching Rob Dow, to come to the kirk to annoy the minister. Ay, he hadna been at that work for ten minutes when Mr. Dishart stopped in his first prayer and ga'e Rob a look. I couldna see the look, being in the precentor's box, but as sure as death I felt it boring through me. Rob is hard wood, though, and soon he was at his tricks again. Weel, the minister stopped a second time in the sermon, and so awful was the silence that a heap o' the congregation couldna keep their seats. I heard Rob breathing quick and strong. Mr. Dishart had his arm pointed at him a' this time, and at last he says, sternly, 'Come forward.' Listen, Joseph Cruickshanks, and tremble. Rob gripped the board to keep himsel' frae obeying, and again Mr. Dishart says, 'Come forward,' and syne Rob rose, shaking, and tottered to the pulpit stair like a man suddenly shot into the Day of Judgment. 'You hulking man of sin,' cries Mr. Dishart, not a tick fleid [afraid], though Rob's as big as three o' him, 'sit down on the stair and attend to me, or I'll step doun frae the pulpit and run you out of the house of God.' "

"And since that day," said Hobart, "Rob has worshipped Mr. Dishart as a man that has stepped out o' the Bible. When the carriage passed this day we was cussing the minister, and Sam'l Dickie wasna sure but what Mr. Dishart wore his hat rather far back on his head. You should have seen Rob. 'My certie,' he roars, 'there's the shine frae Heaven on that little minister's face, and them as says there's no has me to fecht [fight].' "

"Ay, weel," said the U. P., rising, "we'll see how Rob wears — and how your minister wears, too. I wouldna like to sit in a kirk whaur they daurna sing a paraphrase."

"The Psalms of David," retorted Whamond, "mount straight to heaven, but your paraphrases sticks to the ceiling o' the kirk."

"You're a bigoted set, Tammas Whamond, but I tell you this, and it's my last words to you the nicht, the day'll come when you'll hae Mr. Duthie, ay, and even the U.P. minister, preaching in the Auld Licht kirk."

"And let this be my last words to you," replied the precentor, furiously; "that rather than see a U. P. preaching in the Auld Licht kirk I would burn in hell fire for ever!"

This gossip increased Gavin's knowledge of the grim men with whom he had now to deal. But as he sat beside Margaret after she had gone to bed, their talk was pleasant.

"You remember, mother," Gavin said, "how I almost prayed for the manse that was to give you an egg every morning. I have been telling Jean never to forget the egg."

"Ah, Gavin, things have come about so much as we wanted that I'm kind o' troubled. It's hardly natural, and I hope nothing terrible is to happen now."

Gavin arranged her pillows as she liked them, and when he next stole into the room in his stocking soles to look at her, he thought she was asleep. But she was not. I dare say she saw at that moment Gavin in his first frock, and Gavin in knickerbockers, and Gavin as he used to walk into the Glasgow room from college, all still as real to her as the Gavin who had a kirk.

The little minister took away the lamp to his own room, shaking his fist at himself for allowing his mother's door to creak. He pulled up his blind. The town lay still as salt. But a steady light showed in the south, and on pressing his face against the window he saw another in the west. Mr. Carfrae's words about the night-watch came back to him. Perhaps it had been on such a silent night as this that the soldiers marched into Thrums. Would they come again?

13. OUR SERMON TASTER

from *Beside the Bonnie Brier Bush*
by Ian Maclaren (John Watson), 1894

John Watson, who wrote under the pen name of Ian Maclaren, is considered the central figure of that school of fiction to which the Scottish name for a kitchen garden, "kailyard," has been given. Greater writers than he, such as James Barrie and Robert Louis Stevenson, are sometimes identified with the "Kailyard School," at least when they write stories which describe Scottish life in the vernacular. All of Maclaren's work, however, is of this type, and in the beginning of Beside the Bonnie Brier Bush *he quotes:*

There grows a bonnie brier bush in our kail-yard,
And white are the blossoms on't in our kail-yard.

Stern critics today find the sentiment in Watson's stories forced, but lesser mortals will surely still enjoy his "A Doctor of the Old School," from Beside the Bonnie Brier Bush, *or the section given here, "Our Sermon Taster."*

This selection gives some idea of just how central the Sunday church service could be in the intellectual life of a small Scottish village of a century or even less ago. Just as the New England village pictured in Harriet Beecher Stowe's Oldtown Folks *could sharpen its wits by consideration of nice questions of Calvinist doctrine, so Drumtochty men and women are pictured by Maclaren as thinking about the Sabbath throughout the week, and finding in the Sunday sermon a test for their memories, their powers of analysis, and their critical keenness.*

The "Disruption" referred to in this chapter is the crisis of 1843 which established the Free Church of Scotland. (Like the Auld Licht and U.P. churches of the previous chapter, this was a group which broke away from the Established Church.) The Free Church objected particularly to the gradual return, in the Church of Scotland, of patronage — the system customary in England whereby the ministry of a given church was placed under the patronage of a substantial landowner in the area. It also objected to any interference in church matters by civil authorities. The Mistress Stirton who reveals her stupidity in this chapter does so by being unable to answer one of the principal questions of the church's catechism: "What is the chief end of man?"

A Drumtochty man, standing six feet three in his boots, sat himself down one day in the study of a West-end minister, and gazed before him with the countenance of a sphinx.

The sight struck awe into the townsman's heart, and the power of speech was paralyzed within him.

"A'm frae Drumtochty," began a deep solemn voice. "Ye 'ill hae heard of Drumtochty, of coorse. A've jined the polis; the pay is no that bad, and the work is naethin' tae an able-bodied man."

When these particulars had been digested by the audience —

"It's a crooded place London, and the fouk's aye in a tiravie (commotion), rinnin' here an' rinnin' there, and the maist feck [lot] o' them dinna ken whar they're gaein'.

"It's officer this and officer that frae mornin' till nicht. It's peetifu' tae see the helplessness o' the bodies in their ain toon. And they're freevolous," continued the figure, refreshing itself with a reminiscence.

"It was this verra mornin' that a man askit me hoo tae get tae the Strand."

" 'Haud on,' I says, 'till ye come tae a cross street, and dinna gang doon it, and when ye see anither pass it, but whup roond the third, and yir nose 'ill bring ye tae the Strand.' "

"He was a shachlin [infirm] bit cratur, and he lookit up at me.

" 'Where were you born, officer?' in his clippit English tongue.

" 'Drumtochty,' a' said, 'an we hev juist ae man as sma' as you in the hale Glen.'

"He gied awa' laughin' like tae split his sides, an' the fac' is there's no ane o' them asks me a question but he lauchs. They're a licht-headed fouk, and no sair educat. But we maunna boast; they hevna hed oor advantages."

The minister made a brave effort to assert himself.

"Is there anything I can do?" but the figure simply waved its hand and resumed:

"A'm comin' tae that, but a' thocht ye wud be wantin' ma opeenion o' London.

"Weel, ye see, the first thing a' did, of coorse, after settlin' doon, was tae gae roond the kirks and hear what kin' o' ministers they hae up here. A've been in saxteen kirks the last three months, an' a' wud hae been in mair had it no bin for ma 'oors.

"Ay, ay, a' ken ye 'ill be wantin' ma judgment," interpreting a movement in the chair, "an' ye 'll hae it. Some wes puir stuff—plenty o' water and little meal — and some wesna sae bad for England. But ye 'ill be pleased to know," here the figure relaxed and beamed on the anxious minister, "that a'm rael weel satisfied wi' yoursel', and a'm thinkin' o' sittin' under ye.

"Man," were Drumtochty's last words, "a' wish Elspeth Macfadyen cud hear ye, her 'at prees (tastes) the sermons in oor Glen; a' believe she wud pass ye, an' if ye got a certeeficat frae Elspeth, ye wud be a prood man."

Drumtochty read widely — Soutar was soaked in Carlyle, and Marget Howe knew her "In Memoriam" by heart — but our intellectual life centred on the weekly sermon. Men thought about Sabbath as they followed the plough in our caller air, and braced themselves for an effort at the giving out of the text. The hearer had his snuff and selected his attitude, and from that moment to the close he never moved nor took his eyes off the preacher. There was a tradition that one of the Disruption fathers had preached in the Free Kirk for one hour and fifty minutes on the bulwarks of Zion, and had left the impression that he was only playing round the outskirts of his subject. No preacher with anything to say could complain of Drumtochty, for he got a patient, honest, critical hearing from beginning to end. If a preacher were slightly equipped, the audience may have been trying. Well-meaning evangelists who came with what they called "a simple Gospel address," and were accustomed to have their warmer passages punctuated with rounds of spiritual applause in the shape of nods and smiles, lost heart in face of that judicial front, and afterwards described Drumtochty in the religious papers as "dead." It was as well that these good men walked in a vain show, for, as a matter of fact, their hearers were painfully alive.

"Whar did yon wakely body come frae, Burnbrae? it was licht wark the day. There was nae thocht worth mentionin', and onything he hed was eked oot by repeetition. Tae sae neathin' o' bairnly stories [stories for children]."

"He lives aboot England, a'm telt, an' dis a feck o' gude in his ain place. Hesna muckle in his head, a'll alloo that, Netherton, but he's an earnest bit cratur."

"Ou ay, and fu' o' self-conceit. Did ye hear hoo often he said 'I'? a' got as far as saxty-three, and then a' lost count. But a' keepit 'dear,' it cam tae the hundred neat.

" 'Weel?' a' says tae Elspeth Macfadyen. A' kent she wud hae his measure.

" 'Gruel, Netherton, juist gruel, and eneuch [enough] tae scunner (disgust) ye wi' sugar.' "

It was the birthright of every native of the parish to be a critic, and certain were allowed to be experts in special departments — Lachlan Campbell in doctrine and Jamie Soutar in logic — but as an all round practitioner Mrs. Macfadyen had a solitary reputation. It rested on a long series of unreversed judgments, with felicitous strokes of description that passed into the literary capital of the Glen. One felt it was genius, and could only note contributing circumstances — an eye that took in the preacher from the crown of his head to the sole of his foot; an almost uncannie insight into character; the instinct to seize on every scrap of evidence; a memory that was simply an automatic register; an unfailing sense of fitness; and an absolute impartiality regarding subject.

It goes without saying that Mrs. Macfadyen did not take nervous little notes during the sermon — all writing on Sabbath, in kirk or outside, was strictly forbidden in Drumtochty — or mark her Bible, or practise any other profane device of feeble-minded hearers. It did not matter how elaborate or how incoherent a sermon might be, it could not confuse our critic.

When John Peddie of Muirtown, who always

approached two hours, and usually had to leave out the last head, took time at the Drumtochty Fast, and gave, at full length, his famous discourse on the total depravity of the human race, from the text, "Arise, shine, for thy light is come," it may be admitted that the Glen wavered in its confidence. Human nature has limitations, and failure would have been no discredit to Elspeth.

"They were sayin' at the Presbytery," Burnbrae reported, "that it hes mair than seeventy heads [divisions], coontin' pints [sub-divisions], of coorse, and a' can weel believe it. Na, na, it's no tae be expeckit that Elspeth cud gie them a' aifter ae hearin'.''

Jamie Soutar looked in to set his mind at rest, and Elspeth went at once to work.

"Sit doon, Jamie, for it canna be dune in a meenut."

It took twenty-three minutes exactly, for Jamie watched the clock.

"That's the laist, makin' seeventy-four, and ye may depend on every ane but that fourth pint under the sixth head. Whether it was the 'beginnin' o' faith' or 'the origin,' a' canna be sure, for he cleared his throat at the time."

Peter Bruce stood helpless at the Junction next Friday — Drumtochty was celebrating Elspeth — and the achievement established her for life.

Probationers who preached in the vacancy had heard rumours, and tried to identify their judge, with the disconcerting result that they addressed their floweriest passages to Mistress Stirton, who was the stupidest woman in the Free Kirk, and had once stuck in the "chief end of man." They never suspected the sonsy motherly woman, two pews behind Donald Menzies, with her face of demure interest and general air of country simplicity. It was as well for the probationers that they had not caught the glint of those black beady eyes.

"It's curious," Mrs. Macfadyen remarked to me one day, "hoo the pulpit fashions change, juist like weemen's bonnets.

"Noo a' mind when auld Doctor Ferintosh, him 'at wrote 'Judas Iscariot the first Residuary,' would stand twa meenutes facing the fouk, and no sit doon till he hed his snuff.

"But thae young birkies gie oot 'at they see naebody comin' in, an' cover their face wi' ae hand sae solemn, that if ye didna catch them keekin' through their fingers tae see what like the kirk is, ye wud think they were prayin'."

"There's not much escapes you," I dared to say, and although the excellent woman was not accessible to gross flattery, she seemed pleased.

"A'm thankfu that a' can see withoot lookin'; an' a'll wager nae man ever read his sermon in Drumtochty Kirk, an' a' didna find him oot. Noo, there's the new minister o' Netheraird, he writes his sermon on ae side o' ten sheets o' paper, an' he's that carried awa' at the end o' ilka page that he disna ken what he's daein', an' the sleeve o' his goon slips the sheet across tae the ither side o' the Bible.

"But Doctor Ferintosh was cleverer, sall it near beat me tae detect him," and Elspeth paused to enjoy the pulpit ruse. "It cam tae me sudden ae Sacrament Monday, hoo dis he aye turn up twal texts naither mair nor less, and that set me thinkin'. Then a' noticed that he left the Bible open at the place till anither text was due, an' I wunnered a'd been sae slow. It was this wy: he askit the beadle for a glass o' water in the vestry, and slippit his sermon in atween the leaves in sae mony bits. A've wished for a gallery at a time, but there's mair credit in findin' it oot below — ay, an' pleesure tae; a' never wearied in kirk in ma life."

Mrs. Macfadyen did not appreciate prodigal quotations of Scriptures, and had her suspicions of this practice.

"Tak the minister o' Pitscourie noo; he's fair fozzy wi' trokin' in his gairden an' feeding pigs, and hesna studied a sermon for thirty year.

"Sae what dis he dae, think ye? He havers for a while on the errors o' the day, and syne he says, 'That's what man says, but what says the Apostle Paul; We shall see what the Apostle Paul says': He puts on his glasses, and turns up the passage, and reads maybe ten verses, and then he's aff on the jundy (trot) again. When a man hes naethin' tae say he's aye lang, and a've seen him gie half an oor o' passages, and anither half oor o' havers.

" 'He's a Bible preacher, at any rate,' says Burnbrae tae me laist Fast, for, honest man, he hes aye some gude word for a body.

" 'It's ae thing,' I said to him, 'tae feed a calf wi' milk,

and anither tae gie it the empty cogie [wooden dish] tae
lick.'

"It's curious, but a've noticed that when a Moderate
gets lazy he preaches auld sermons, but a Free Kirk
minister taks tae abusing his neeburs and readin' screeds
o' the Bible.

"But Maister Pittendreigh hes twa sermons, at ony
rate," and Elspeth tasted the sweets of memory with
such keen relish that I begged for a share.

"Well, ye see he's terrible prood o' his feenishes, and
this is ane o' them:

" 'Heaven, me brethren, will be far grander than the
hoose o' ony earthly potentate, for there ye will no
longer eat the flesh of bulls nor drink the blood o' goats,
but we shall sook the juicy pear and scoop the loocious
meelon. Amen.'

"He hes nae mair sense o' humor than an owl, and a'
aye haud that a man withoot humor sudna be allowed
intae a poopit.

"A' hear that they have nae examination in humor at
the college; it's an awfu' want, for it wud keep oot
mony a dreich [tedious] body.

"But the meelon's naethin' tae the goat, that cowed
a' thing [bested everything], at the Fast tae."

"If Jeems wes aboot a' daurna mention 't: he canna
behave himsel' tae this day gin he hears 't, though ye
ken he's a douce [sober] man as ever lived.

"It was anither feenish, and it ran this wy:

" 'Noo, ma freends, a' wull no be keepin' ye ony
longer, and ye 'ill a' gae hame tae yir ain hooses and

mind yir ain business. And as sune as ye get hame ilka man 'ill gae tae his closet and shut the door, and stand for five meenutes, and ask himsel' this solemn question, "Am I a goat?" Amen.'

"The amen near upset me masel' [myself], and a' hed tae dunge Jeems wi' ma elbow.

"He said no a word on the wy back, but a' saw it wes barmin' in him, and he gied oot sudden aifter his dinner as if he had been ta'en unweel.

"A' cam' on him in the byre [cow-house], rowing [rolling] in the strae like a bairn, and every ither row he took he wud say, 'Am I a goat?'

"It wes no cannie [wise] for a man o' his wecht, besides bein' a married man and a kirk member, and a' gied him a hearing.

"He sobered doon, and a' never saw him dae the like since. But he hesna forgot, na, na; a've seen a look come ower Jeems' face in kirk, and a've been feared."

When the Free Kirk quarrelled in their vacancy over two probationers, Mrs. Macfadyen summed them up with such excellent judgment that they were thrown over and peace restored.

"There's some 'o thae Muirtown drapers can busk oot their windows that ye canna pass withoot lookin'; there's bits o' blue and bits o' red, and a ribbon here an' a lace yonder.

"It's a bonnie show and denty, an' no wunner the lassies stan' and stare.

"But gae intae the shop, and peety me, there's next tae naethin'; it's a' in the window.

"Noo, that's Maister Popinjay, as neat an' fikey [fidgety] a little mannie as ever a' saw in a black goon.

"His bit sermon was six poems — five a' hed heard afore — four anecdotes — three aboot himsel' and ain aboot a lord — twa burnies, ae floo'r gairden, and a snowstorm, wi' the text thirteen times and 'beloved' twal; that was a'; a takin' window, and Netherton's lassies cudna sleep thinkin' o' him.

"There's ither shopmen in Muirtown that fair scunner ye wi' their windows — they're that ill set out — and inside there's sic a wale o' stuff that the man canna get what ye want; he's clean smoored wi' his ain goods.

"It's a graund shop for the auld fouk that hae plenty o' time and can turn ower the things by the 'oor. Ye 'ill no get a young body inside the door.

"That's Maister Auchtermuchty; he hes mair material than he kens hoo tae handle, and naebody, hearin' him, can mak head or tail o' his sermon.

"Ye get a rive [burst] at the Covenants ae meenute, and a mouthfu' o' justification the next. Yir nae suner wi' the Patriarchs than yir whuppit aff tae the Apostles.

"It's rich feedin', nae doot, but sair mixed, an' no verra tasty."

So the old and young compromised, and chose Carmichael.

Elspeth was candid enough on occasion, but she was not indiscreet. She could convey her mind delicately if need be, and was a mistress of subtle suggestion.

When Netherton's nephew preached the missionary sermon — he was a stout young man with a volcanic voice — Mrs. Macfadyen could not shirk her duty, but she gave her judgment with care.

"He's a fine lad, and 'ill be sure to get a kirk; he's been weel brocht up, and comes o' decent fouk.

"His doctrine soonds richt, an' he 'ill no gang aff the track. Ye canna ca' him bashfu', and he's sure to be heard."

Her audience still waited, and not in vain.

"But the Lord hes nae pleesure in the legs o' a man," and every one felt that the last word had been said on Netherton's nephew.

14. CHAPTER FOUR

from *In His Steps*
by Charles M. Sheldon, 1896

Since over twenty million copies of Charles M. Sheldon's In His Steps *have been sold, it must be presumed that many readers of our own time know this most extraordinary of best sellers. It can be taken for granted, however, that almost no one who could read, and who was of reading age between 1896 and 1906, was unaware of the book. The Reverend Mr. Sheldon wrote the story in 1896, read it a chapter at a time during Sunday evening "young people's meetings" in the Central Congregational Church of Topeka, Kansas, and published it serially in the* Chicago Advance, *a religious weekly. Because of faulty provisions to fulfill copyright regulations, the book was thrown into the "public domain." Within a few years sixteen publishers in America and fifty in Europe and Australia had published editions of the book, one London publisher selling three million copies at a penny each on the streets of London. The story has been translated into twenty-one languages, and the Russian version has been banned in Soviet Russia.*

A recent paperback edition (Permabook, 1949) includes Mr. Sheldon's statement that the book's success "confirms the faith I have always held that no subject is more interesting and vital to the human race than religion." It may be that the phenomenal success of this particular story has something also to do with the simplicity and literalness with which the author presents an ethical lesson. In His Steps tells the story of a group of church people in an American town who decide to ask themselves the question, "What would Jesus do?" before making any decision in the conduct of their daily lives. If it is difficult for some of us to imagine first century Palestine in juxtaposition to nineteenth-century-America, it may have been the very forthrightness of this idea which appealed strongly to readers in a time when the mystical side of religion was receiving little attention from the average Protestant church-goer, and when the Darwinian controversy seemed to be "calling all in doubt."

The chapter given here describes public reaction to the decision of the newspaper editor, Edward Norman, not to print news of the big prize fight which took place a few days before the opening of the chapter.

❖ ◆ ❖

During the week he was in receipt of numerous letters commenting on the absence from the *News* of the account of the prize fight. Two or three of these letters may be of interest.

> Editor of the *News:*
>
> Dear Sir — I have been thinking for some time of changing my paper. I want a journal that is up to the times, progressive and enterprising, supplying the public demand at all points. The recent freak of your paper in refusing to print the account of the famous contest at the Resort has decided me finally to change my paper. Please discontinue it.
>
> Very truly yours,
>
> _____

Here followed the name of a business man who had been a subscriber for many years.

> Edward Norman,
> Editor of the *Daily News,* Raymond:
>
> Dear Ed. — What is this sensation you have given the people of your burg? What new policy have you taken up? Hope you don't intend to try the "Reform Business" through the avenue of the press. It's dangerous to experiment much along that line. Take my advice and stick to the enterprising modern methods you have made so successful for the *News.* The public wants prize fights and such. Give it what it wants, and let some one else do the Reforming business.
>
> Yours,
>
> _____

Here followed the name of one of Norman's old friends, the editor of a daily in an adjoining town.

> My Dear Mr. Norman:
>   I hasten to write you a note of appreciation for the evident carrying out of your promise. It is a splendid beginning and no one feels the value of it more than I do. I know something of what it will cost you, but not all.
>
>   Your pastor,
>   Henry Maxwell

One other letter which he opened immediately after reading this from Maxwell revealed to him something of the loss to his business that possibly awaited him.

> Mr. Edward Norman:
> Editor of the *Daily News:*
>   Dear Sir — At the expiration of my advertising limit, you will do me the favor not to continue it as you have done heretofore. I enclose check for payment in full and shall consider my account with your paper closed after date.
>
>   Very truly yours,
>   ———————————

Here followed the name of one of the largest dealers in tobacco in the city. He had been in the habit of inserting a column of conspicuous advertising and paying for it a very large price.

Norman laid this letter down thoughtfully, and then

after a moment he took up a copy of his paper and looked through the advertising columns. There was no connection implied in the tobacco merchant's letter between the omission of the prize fight and the withdrawal of the advertisement, but he could not avoid putting the two together. In point of fact, he afterward learned that the tobacco dealer withdrew his advertisement because he had heard that the editor of the *News* was about to enter upon some queer reform policy that would be certain to reduce its subscription list.

But the letter directed Norman's attention to the advertising phase of his paper. He had not considered this before.

As he glanced over the columns he could not escape the conviction that his Master could not permit some of them in his paper.

What would He do with that other long advertisement of choice liquors and cigars? As a member of a church and a respected citizen, he had incurred no special censure because the saloon men advertised in his columns. No one thought anything about it. It was all legitimate business. Why not? Raymond enjoyed a system of high license, and the saloon and the billiard hall and the beer garden were a part of the city's Christian civilization. He was simply doing what every other business man in Raymond did. And it was one of the best paying sources of revenue. What would the paper do if it cut these out? Could it live? That was the question. But — was that the question after all? "What would Jesus do?" That was the question he was answering, or trying to answer, this week. Would Jesus advertise whiskey and tobacco in his paper?

Edward Norman asked it honestly, and after a prayer for help and wisdom he asked Clark to come to his office.

Clark came in, feeling that the paper was at a crisis, and prepared for almost anything after his Monday morning experience. This was Thursday.

"Clark," said Norman, speaking slowly and carefully, "I have been looking at our advertising columns and have decided to dispense with some of the matter as soon as the contracts run out. I wish you would notify the advertising agent not to solicit or renew the ads that I have marked here."

He handed the paper with the marked places over to Clark, who took it and looked over the columns with a very serious air.

"This will mean a great loss to the *News*. How long do you think you can keep this sort of thing up?" Clark was astounded at the editor's action and could not understand it.

"Clark, do you think if Jesus was the editor and proprietor of a daily paper in Raymond He would permit advertisements of whiskey and tobacco in it?"

"Well — no — I don't suppose He would. But what has that to do with us? We can't do business as He would. Newspapers can't be run on any such basis."

"Why not?" asked Norman quietly.

"Why not? Because they will lose more money than

they make, that's all!" Clark spoke out with an irritation that he really felt. "We shall certainly bankrupt the paper with this sort of business policy."

"Do you think so?" Norman asked the question not as if he expected an answer, but simply as if he were talking with himself. After a pause he said:

"You may direct Marks to do as I have said. I believe it is what Christ would do, and as I told you, Clark, that is what I have promised to try to do for a year, regardless of what the results may be to me. I cannot believe that by any kind of reasoning we could reach a conclusion justifying our Lord in the advertisement, in this age, of whiskey and tobacco in a newspaper. There are some other advertisements of a doubtful character I shall study into. Meanwhile, I feel a conviction in regard to these that cannot be silenced."

Clark went back to his desk feeling as if he had been in the presence of a very peculiar person. He could not grasp the meaning of it all. He felt enraged and alarmed. He was sure any such policy would ruin the paper as soon as it became generally known that the editor was trying to do everything by such an absurd moral standard. What would become of business if this standard was adopted? It would upset every custom and introduce endless confusion. It was simply foolishness. It was downright idiocy. So Clark said to himself, and when Marks was informed of the action he seconded the managing editor with some very forcible ejaculations. What was the matter with the chief? Was he going to bankrupt the whole business?

But Edward Norman had not yet faced his most serious problem. When he came down to the office Friday morning he was confronted with the usual program for the Sunday morning edition. The *News* was one of the few evening papers in Raymond to issue a Sunday edition, and it had always been remarkably successful financially. There was an average of one page of literary and religious items to thirty or forty pages of sport, theatre, gossip, fashion, society and political material. This made a very interesting magazine of all sorts of reading matter, and had always been welcomed by all the subscribers, church members and all, as a Sunday morning necessity.

Edward Norman now faced this fact and put to himself the question: "What would Jesus do?" If He was editor of a paper, would He deliberately plan to put into the homes of all the church people and Christians of Raymond such a collection of reading matter on the one day in the week which ought to be given up to something better and holier? He was of course familiar with the regular arguments of the Sunday paper, that the public needed something of the sort; and the working man especially, who would not go to church anyway, ought to have something entertaining and instructive on Sunday, his only day of rest. But suppose the Sunday morning paper did not pay? Suppose there was no money in it? How eager would the editor or publisher be then to supply this crying need of the poor workman? Edward Norman communed honestly with himself over the subject.

Taking everything into account, would Jesus probably edit a Sunday morning paper? No matter what it paid. That was not the question. As a matter of fact, the Sunday *News* paid so well that it would be a direct loss of thousands of dollars to discontinue it. Besides, the regular subscribers had paid for a seven-day paper. Had he any right now to give them less than they supposed they had paid for?

He was honestly perplexed by the question. So much was involved in the discontinuance of the Sunday edition that for the first time he almost decided to refuse to be guided by the standard of Jesus' probable action. He was sole proprietor of the paper; it was his to shape as he chose. He had no board of directors to consult as to policy. But as he sat there surrounded by the usual quantity of material for the Sunday edition he reached some definite conclusions. And among them was a determination to call in the force of the paper and frankly state his motive and purpose. He sent word for Clark and the other men in the office, including the few reporters who were in the building and the foreman, with what men were in the composing room (it was early in the morning and they were not all in) to come into the mailing room. This was a large room, and the men came in curiously and perched around on the tables and counters. It was a very unusual proceeding, but they all agreed that the paper was being run on a new principle anyhow, and they all watched Mr. Norman carefully as he spoke.

"I called you in here to let you know my further

plans for the *News*. I propose certain changes which I believe are necessary. I understand very well that some things I have already done are regarded by the men as very strange. I wish to state my motive in doing what I have done."

Here he told the men what he had already told Clark, and they stared as Clark had done, and looked as painfully conscious.

"Now, in acting on this standard of conduct I have reached a conclusion which will, no doubt, cause some surprise.

"I have decided that the Sunday morning edition of the *News* shall be discontinued after next Sunday's issue. I shall state in that issue my reasons for discontinuing. In order to make up to the subscribers the amount of reading matter they may suppose themselves entitled to, we can issue a double number on Saturday, as is done by many evening papers that make no attempt at a Sunday edition. I am convinced that from a Christian point of view more harm than good has been done by our Sunday morning paper. I do not believe that Jesus would be responsible for it if He were in my place today. It will occasion some trouble to arrange the details caused by this change with the advertisers and subscribers. This is for me to look after. The change itself is one that will take place. So far as I can see, the loss will fall on myself. Neither the reporters nor the pressmen need make any particular changes in their plans."

He looked around the room and no one spoke. He

was struck for the first time in his life with the fact that in all the years of his newspaper life he had never had the force of the paper together in this way. Would Jesus do that? That is, would He probably run a newspaper on some loving family plan, where editors, reporters, pressmen and all meet to discuss and devise and plan for the making of a paper that should have in view —

He caught himself drawing almost away from the facts of typographical unions and office rules and reporters' enterprise and all the cold, businesslike methods that make a great daily successful. But still the vague picture that came up in the mailing room would not fade away when he had gone into his office and the men had gone back to their places with wonder in their looks and questions of all sorts on their tongues as they talked over the editor's remarkable actions.

Clark came in and had a long, serious talk with his chief. He was thoroughly roused, and his protest almost reached the point of resigning his place. Norman guarded himself carefully. Every minute of the interview was painful to him, but he felt more than ever the necessity of doing the Christ-like thing. Clark was a very valuable man. It would be difficult to fill his place. But he was not able to give any reasons for continuing the Sunday paper that answered the question, "What would Jesus do?" by letting Jesus print that edition.

"It comes to this, then," said Clark frankly, "you will bankrupt the paper in thirty days. We might as well face that future fact."

"I don't think we shall. Will you stay by the *News*

until it is bankrupt?" asked Norman with a strange smile.

"Mr. Norman, I don't understand you. You are not the same man this week that I always knew before."

"I don't know myself either, Clark. Something remarkable has caught me up and borne me on. But I was never more convinced of final success and power for the paper. You have not answered my question. Will you stay with me?"

Clark hesitated a moment and finally said yes. Norman shook hands with him and turned to his desk. Clark went back into his room, stirred by a number of conflicting emotions. He had never before known such an exciting and mentally disturbing week, and he felt now as if he was connected with an enterprise that might at any moment collapse and ruin him and all connected with it.

15. FEEDING OF THE PIGS

from *Lorna Doone* [Chapt. XXXII]
by R. D. Blackmore, 1869

This is the second chapter from Blackmore's Lorna
Doone *to be included in this book, but surely even so
anonymous a thing as an editor may be allowed a
favorite. The story has gone on until Lorna is virtually a
prisoner among those whom she presumes to be her kin,
the savage Doones, and John Ridd is wild to get her
away from them and make her his wife. Lovers today
may not express their enthusiasm by kissing the
messenger who brings good news; but even if the
modern person's approach may be a little more direct,
that is not necessarily a sign that feelings run deeper
than those of the man who loved Lorna.*

The story told by John Fry that night, and my conviction of the truth, made me very uneasy, especially as

following upon the warning of Judge Jeffreys, and the hints received from Jeremy Stickles, and the outburst of the tanner at Dunster, as well as sundry tales and rumours, and signs of secret understanding, seen and heard on market-days, and at places of entertainment. We knew for certain that at Taunton, Bridgewater, and even Dulverton, there was much disaffection toward the King, and regret for the days of the Puritans. Albeit I had told the truth, and the pure and simple truth, when, upon my examination, I had assured his lordship that to the best of my knowledge there was nothing of the sort with us.

But now I was beginning to doubt whether I might not have been mistaken; especially when we heard, as we did, of arms being landed at Lynmouth in the dead of the night, and of the tramp of men having reached some one's ears from a hill where a famous echo was. For it must be plain to any conspirator (without the example of the Doones) that for the secret muster of men, and the stowing of unlawful arms, and communication by beacon lights, scarcely a fitter place could be found than the wilds of Exmoor, with deep ravines running far inland from an unwatched and mostly a sheltered sea. For the channel from Countisbury Foreland up to Minehead, or even further, though rocky and gusty, and full of currents, is safe from great rollers, and the sweeping power of the southwest storms, which prevail with us more than all others, and make sad work on the opposite coast.

But even supposing it probable that something against

King Charles the Second (or rather against his Roman advisers, and especially his brother) were now in preparation among us, was it likely that Master Huckaback, a wealthy man, and a careful one, known moreover to the Lord Chief-justice, would have anything to do with it? To this I could make no answer; Uncle Ben was so close a man, so avaricious, and so revengeful, that it was quite impossible to say what course he might pursue, without knowing all the chances of gain, or rise, or satisfaction to him. That he hated the Papists, I knew full well, though he never spoke much about them; also that he had followed the march of Oliver Cromwell's army, but more as a sutler (people said) than as a real soldier; and that he would go a long way, and risk a great deal of money, to have his revenge on the Doones; although their name never passed his lips during the present visit.

But how was it likely to be as to the Doones themselves? Which side would they probably take in the coming movement, if movement it would be? So far as they had any religion at all, by birth they were Roman Catholics — so much I knew from Lorna; and indeed it was well known all around, that a priest had been fetched more than once to the valley to soothe some poor outlaw's departure. On the other hand they were not likely to entertain much affection for the son of the man who had banished them and confiscated their property. And it was not at all impossible that desperate men, such as they were, having nothing to lose, but estates to recover, and not being held by religion much, should cast away all regard for the birth from which they had been cast out, and make common cause with a Protestant rising for the chance of revenge and re-placement.

However, I do not mean to say that all these things occurred to me as clearly as I have set them down; only that I was in general doubt, and very sad perplexity. For mother was so warm, and innocent, and so kind to every one, that knowing some little by this time of the English constitution, I feared very greatly lest she should be punished for harboring malcontents. As well as possible I knew that if any poor man came to our door, and cried, "Officers are after me; for God's sake take and hide me," mother would take him in at once, and con-ceal and feed him, even though he had been very vio-lent; and, to tell the truth, so would both my sisters, and so indeed would I do. Whence it will be clear that we were not the sort of people to be safe among disturbances.

Before I could quite make up my mind how to act in this difficulty, and how to get at the rights of it (for I would not spy after Uncle Reuben, though I felt no great fear of the Wizard's Slough, and none of the man with white night-cap), a difference came again upon it, and a change of chances. For Uncle Reuben went away as suddenly as he first had come to us, giving no reason for his departure, neither claiming the pony, and indeed leaving something behind him of great value to my mother. For he begged her to see to his young grand-daughter until he could find opportunity of fetching her safely to Dulverton. Mother was overjoyed at this, as she could not help displaying; and Ruth was quite as much

delighted, although she durst not show it. For at
Dulverton she had to watch and keep such ward on the
victuals, and the in and out of the shopmen, that it went
entirely against her heart, and she never could enjoy
herself. Truly she was an altered girl from the day she
came to us; catching our unsuspicious manners, and our
free good-will, and hearty noise of laughing.

By this time, the harvest being done, and the thatch-
ing of the ricks made sure against south-western tem-
pests, and all the reapers being gone, with good money
and thankfulness, I began to burn in spirit for the sight
of Lorna. I had begged my sister Annie to let Sally
Snowe know, once for all, that it was not in my power
to have anything more to do with her. Of course our
Annie was not to grieve Sally, neither let it appear for a
moment that I suspected her kind views upon me, and
her strong regard for our dairy: only I thought it right
upon our part not to waste Sally's time any longer,
being a handsome wench as she was, and many young
fellows glad to marry her.

And Annie did this uncommonly well, as she herself
told me afterward, having taken Sally in the sweetest
manner into her pure confidence, and opened half her
bosom to her about my very sad love-affair. Not that
she let Sally know, of course, who it was, or what it
was; only that she made her understand, without hinting
at my desire of it, that there was no chance now of
having me. Sally changed color a little at this, and then
went on about a red cow which had passed seven
needles at milking-time.

Inasmuch as there are two sorts of month well recognized by the calendar, to-wit, the lunar and the solar, I made bold to regard both my months, in the absence of any provision, as intended to be strictly lunar. Therefore, upon the very day when the eight weeks were expiring, forth I went in search of Lorna, taking the pearl ring hopefully, and all the newlaid eggs I could find, and a dozen and a half of small trout from our brook. And the pleasure it gave me to catch those trout, thinking, as every one came forth and danced upon the grass, how much she would enjoy him, is more than I can now describe, although I well remember it. And it struck me that after accepting my ring, and saying how much she loved me, it was possible that my queen might invite me even to stay and sup with her; and so I arranged with dear Annie beforehand, who now was the greatest comfort to me, to account for my absence if I should be late.

But alas, I was utterly disappointed; for although I waited and waited for hours, with an equal amount both of patience and peril, no Lorna ever appeared at all, nor even the faintest sign of her. And another thing occurred as well, which vexed me more than it need have done, for so small a matter. And this was that my little offering of the trout and new-laid eggs were carried off in the coolest manner by that vile Carver Doone. For thinking to keep them the fresher and nicer, away from so much handling, I laid them in a little bed of reeds by the side of the water, and placed some dog-leaves over them. And when I had quite forgotten about them, and was watching from my hiding-place beneath the willow-tree (for I liked not to enter Lorna's bower without her permission, except just to peep that she was not there), and while I was turning the ring in my pocket, having just seen the new moon, I became aware of a great man coming leisurely down the valley. He had a broad-brimmed hat, and a leather jerkin, and heavy jackboots to his middle thigh, and, what was worst of all for me, on his shoulder he bore a long carbine. Having nothing to meet him withal but my staff, and desiring to avoid disturbance, I retired promptly into the chasm, keeping the tree betwixt us that he might not descry me, and watching behind the jut of a rock, where now I had scraped myself a neat little hole for the purpose.

Presently the great man reappeared, being now within fifty yards of me, and the light still good enough, as he drew nearer, for me to descry his features; and though I am not a judge of men's faces, there was something in his which turned me cold, as though with a kind of horror. Not that it was an ugly face; nay, rather it seemed a handsome one, so far as mere form and line might go; full of strength, and vigor, and will, and stead-fast resolution. From the short black hair above the broad forehead, to the long black beard descending below the curt bold chin, there was not any curve or glimpse of weakness or of after-thought; nothing play-ful, nothing pleasant, nothing like a track for smiles; nothing which a friend could like, and laugh at him for having. And yet he might have been a good man (for I have known very good men so fortified by their own strange ideas of God): I say that he might have seemed a good man, but for the cold and cruel hankering of his steel-blue eyes.

Now let no one suppose for a minute that I saw all this in a moment; for I am very slow, and take a long time to digest things; only I like to set down, and have done with it, all the results of my knowledge, though they be not manifold. But what I said to myself just then was no more than this: "What a fellow to have Lorna!" Having my sense of right so outraged (although of course, I would never allow her to go so far as that), I almost longed that he might thrust his head in to look after me. For there I was, with my ash staff clubbed, ready to have at him, and not ill inclined to do so if only he would come where strength, not fire-arms, must decide it. However, he suspected nothing of my dangerous neighbourhood, but walked his round like a sentinel, and turned at the brink of the water.

Then, as he marched back again along the margin of the stream, he espied my little hoard, covered up with dog-leaves. He saw that the leaves were upside down, and this of course drew his attention. I saw him stoop and lay bare the fish, and the eggs set a little way from them; and in my simple heart I thought that now he knew all about me. But, to my surprise, he seemed well pleased; and his harsh, short laughter came to me without echo —

"Ha, ha! Charlie boy! Fisherman Charlie, have I caught thee setting bait for Lorna? Now I understand thy fishings and the robbing of Counselor's hen-roost.

May I never have good roasting, if I have it not to-night, and roast thee, Charlie, afterward!"

With this he calmly packed up my fish, and all the best of dear Annie's eggs, and went away, chuckling steadfastly, to his home, if one may call it so. But I was so thoroughly grieved and mortified by this most impudent robbery, that I started forth from my rocky screen with the intention of pursuing him, until my better sense arrested me, barely in time to escape his eyes. For I said to myself, that even supposing that I could contend unarmed with him, it would be the greatest folly in the world to have my secret access known, and perhaps a fatal barrier placed between Lorna and myself, and I knew not what trouble brought upon her, all for the sake of a few eggs and fishes. It was better to bear this trifling loss, however ignominious and goading to the spirit, than to risk my love and Lorna's welfare, and perhaps be shot into the bargain. And I think that all will agree with me that I acted for the wisest, in withdrawing to my shelter, though deprived of eggs and fishes.

Having waited (as I said) until there was no chance whatever of my love appearing. I hastened homeward very sadly; and the wind of early autumn moaned across the moor-land. All the beauty of the harvest, all the gayety was gone, and the early fall of dusk was like a weight upon me. Nevertheless, I went every evening thenceforward for a fortnight; hoping, every time in vain, to find my hope and comfort. And meanwhile what perplexed me most was that the signals were replaced, in order as agreed upon, so that Lorna could scarcely be restrained by any rigor.

One time I had a narrow chance of being shot and settled with; and it befell me thus. I was waiting very carelessly, being now a little desperate, at the entrance to the glen, instead of watching through my sight-hole, as the proper practice was. Suddenly a ball went by me with a whizz and whistle, passing through my hat, and sweeping it away all folded up. My soft hat fluttered far down the stream before I had time to go after it, and with the help of wind and water, was fifty yards gone in a moment. At this I had just enough mind left to shrink back very suddenly, and lurk very still and closely; for I knew what a narrow escape it had been, as I heard the bullet, hard set by the powder, sing mournfully down the chasm, like a drone banished out of the hive. And as I peered through my little cranny, I saw a wreath of smoke still floating where the thickness was of the withy-bed; and presently Carver Doone came forth, having stopped to reload his piece perhaps, and ran very swiftly to the entrance to see what he had shot.

Sore trouble had I to keep close quarters, from the slipperiness of the stone beneath me, with the water sliding over it. My foe came quite to the verge of the fall, where the river began to comb over; and there he stopped for a minute or two, on the utmost edge of dry land, upon the very spot indeed where I had fallen senseless when I climbed it in my boyhood. I could hear him breathing hard and grunting, as in doubt and discontent, for he stood within a yard of me, and I kept my fist ready for him if he should discover me. Then at the foot of the water-slide my black hat suddenly appeared, tossing in white foam, and fluttering like a raven wounded. Now I had doubted which hat to take when I had left home that day; till I thought that the black became me best, and might seem kinder to Lorna.

"Have I killed thee, old bird, at last?" my enemy cried in triumph; "'tis the third time I have shot at thee, and thou wast beginning to mock me. No more of thy cursed croaking now, to wake me in the morning. Ha, ha! there are not many who get three chances from Carver Doone; and none will ever go beyond it."

I laughed within myself at this, as he strode away in his triumph; for was not this his third chance of me, and he no whit the wiser? And then I thought that perhaps the chance might some day be on the other side.

For, to tell the truth, I was heartily tired of lurking and playing bo-peep so long; to which nothing could have reconciled me except my fear for Lorna. And here I saw was a man of strength fit for me to encounter such as I had never met, but would be glad to meet with; having found no man of late who needed not my mercy at wrestling or at single-stick. And growing more and more uneasy as I found no Lorna, I would have tried to force the Doone Glen from the upper end, and take my chance of getting back, but for Annie and her prayers.

Now, that same night I think it was, or at any rate the next one, that I noticed Betty Muxworthy going on most strangely. She made the queerest signs to me when nobody was looking, and laid her fingers on her lips, and pointed over her shoulder. But I took little heed of her, being in a kind of dudgeon, and oppressed with evil luck; believing, too, that all she wanted was to have some little grumble about some petty grievance.

But presently she poked me with the heel of a fire-bundle, and, passing close to my ear, whispered, so that none else could hear her, "Larna Doo-un."

By these words I was so startled, that I turned round and stared at her; but she pretended not to know it, and began with all her might to scour an empty crock with a besom.

"Oh, Betty, let me help you. That work is much too hard for you," I cried, with a sudden chivalry, which only won rude answer.

"Zeed me a-dooing of thic every naight last ten year, Jan, wiout vindin out how hard it wor. But if so be thee wants to help, carr peg's bucket for me. Massy, if I ain't forgotten to fade the pegs till now."

Favoring me with another wink, to which I now paid the keenest heed, Betty went and fetched the lantern from the hook inside the door. Then, when she had kindled it, not allowing me any time to ask what she was after, she went outside, and pointed to the great bock of wash, and riddlings, and brown hulkage (for we ground our own corn always); and though she knew that Bill Dadds and Jem Slocombe had full work to carry it on a pole (with another to help to sling it), she said to me as quietly as a maiden might ask one to carry a glove, "Jan Ridd, carr thic thing for me."

So I carried it for her without any words, wondering what she was up to next, and whether she had ever heard of being too hard on the willing horse. And when we came to hog-pound, she turned upon me suddenly, with the lantern she was bearing, and saw that I had the bock by one hand very easily.

"Jan Ridd," she said, "there be no other man in England cud a' dood it. Now thee shalt have Larna."

While I was wondering how my chance of having Lorna could depend upon my power to carry pig's-wash, and how Betty could have any voice in the matter (which seemed to depend upon her decision), and in short, while I was all abroad as to her knowledge and everything, the pigs, who had been fast asleep and dreaming in their emptiness, awoke with one accord at the goodness of the smell around them. They had resigned themselves, as even pigs do, to a kind of fast, hoping to break their fast more sweetly on the morrow morning. But now they tumbled out all headlong, pigs below and pigs above, pigs point-blank and pigs across, pigs courant and pigs rampant, but all alike prepared to eat, and all in good cadence squeaking.

"Tak smarl booket, and bale un out; wad e' waste sich stoof as thic here be?" So Betty set me to feed the pigs, while she held the lantern; and knowing what she was, I saw that she would not tell me another word until all the pigs were served. And in truth no man could well look at them and delay to serve them, they were all expressing appetite in so forceful a manner; some running to and fro, and rubbing and squealing as if from starvation, some rushing down to the oaken troughs, and poking each other away from them; and the kindest of all putting up their fore feet on the top rail of the hog-pound, and blinking their little eyes, and grunting prettily to coax us; as who should say, "I trust you now; you will be kind, I know, and give me the first and the very best of it."

"Oppen ge-at now, wull 'e, Jan? Maind, young sow wi' the baible back arlway hath first toorn of it, 'cos I brought her up on my lap, I did. Zuck, zuck, zuck! How her stickth her tail up; do me good to zee un! Now thiccy trough, thee zany, and tak thee girt legs out o' the wai. Wish they wud gie thee a good baite, mak thee hop a bit vaster, I reckon. Hit that there girt ozebird over's back wi' the broomstick, he be robbing of my young zow. Choog, choog, choog! and a drap more left in the dippingpail."

"Come now, Betty," I said, when all the pigs were at it, sucking, swilling, munching, guzzling, thrusting, and ousting, and spilling the food upon the backs of their brethren (as great men do with their charity). "Come now, Betty, how much longer am I to wait for your message? Surely I am as good as a pig."

"Dunno as thee be, Jan. No strakiness in thy bakkon. And now I come to think of it, Jan, thee zed, a wake agone last Vriday, as how I had got a girt be-ard. Wull 'e stick to that now, Maister Jan?"

"No, no, Betty, certainly not; I made a mistake about it. I should have said a becoming mustache, such as you may well be proud of."

"Then thee be a liar, Jan Ridd. Zay so, laike a man, lad."

"Not exactly that, Betty; but I made a great mistake:

and I humbly ask your pardon; and if such a thing as a crown-piece, Betty —"

"No fai, no fai!" said Betty; however she put it into her pocket; "now tak my advice, Jan; thee marry Zally Snowe."

"Not with all England for her dowry. Oh Betty, you know better."

"Ah's me! I know much worse, Jan. Break thy poor mother's heart it will. And to think of arl the dannger! Dost love Larna now so much?"

"With all the strength of my heart and soul. I will have her, or I will die, Betty."

"Wull, thee will die in aither case. But it baint for me to argify. And do her love thee too, Jan?"

"I hope she does, Betty. I hope she does. What do you think about it?"

"Ah, then I may hold my tongue to it. Knaw what boys and maidens be, as well as I knaw young pegs. I myzell been o' that zort one taime every bit so well as you be." And Betty held the lantern up, and defied me to deny it; and the light through the horn showed a gleam in her eyes such as I had never seen there before. "No odds, no odds about that," she continued; "mak a fool of myzell to spake of it. Arl gone into church-yard. But it be a lucky foolery for thee, my boy. I can tull 'ee. For I love to see the love in thee. Coom'th over me as the spring do, though I be naigh three-score. Now, Jan, I will tell thee one thing, can't abear to zee vretting so. Hould thee head down, same as they pegs do."

So I bent my head quite close to her; and she

whispered in my ear, "Goo of a marning, thee girt soft. Her can't get out of an avening now; her hath zent word to me, to tull 'ee."

In the glory of my delight at this, I bestowed upon Betty a chaste salute, with all the pigs for witnesses; and she took it not amiss, considering how long she had been out of practice. But then she fell back, like a broom on its handle, and stared at me, feigning anger.

"Oh fai, oh fai! Lunnon impudence, I doubt. I vear thee hast gone on zadly, Jan."

BIBLIOGRAPHICAL NOTES

Eight books among the fourteen represented in this sampler were published late enough (1894 or thereafter) to be included in *The Bookman's* monthly lists of "best sellers" in the United States. Five of these eight appeared on these lists at least once, and several for many months in succession. The five are *Beside the Bonnie Brier Bush, In His Steps, Mrs. Wiggs of the Cabbage Patch, T. Tembarom,* and *When Knighthood Was in Flower*. Only four of the fourteen books included in this volume are now out of print — and three of these four were among the "best sellers" of their day: *When Knighthood Was in Flower, T. Tembarom,* and *Beside the Bonnie Brier Bush*. To capture the fancy of the moment is not, apparently, necessarily to ensure an enduring place on readers' bookshelves. The books discussed below are placed in the order in which they appear in the anthology.

TOM BROWN AT OXFORD

Thomas Hughes' (1822–1896) *Tom Brown at Oxford,* now available in three editions in England, was published in 1861 by Macmillan, capitalizing on the success of the better known *Tom Brown's Schooldays,* first published in 1857 and running to five editions within nine months. *Tom Brown's Schooldays* remains one of Macmillan's enduring favorites to this day.

THE BIBLE IN SPAIN

After years of unsuccessful attempts to interest publishers and the reading public in such obscure works as *Romantic Ballads,* translated from the Danish, George Borrow (1803–1881) persuaded the prominent London publisher, John Murray, to bring out what proved to be his masterpiece. The date was 1842, and the whole imposing title of the three-volume work is *The Bible in Spain; or The Journeys, Adventures, and Imprisonments of an Englishman in an Attempt to Circulate the Scriptures in the Peninsula.* Borrow's *The "Zincali"; or, An Account of the Gypsies of Spain,* published in 1841, "with an original collection of their songs and poetry, and a copious dictionary of their language," and also brought out by John Murray, had scarcely sold the 750 copies originally printed. *The Bible in Spain,* however, was an immediate success. The first edition of a thousand copies was soon exhausted, and seven more editions were brought out during 1843. Indeed, the success of the work encouraged Murray to bring out two additional editions of *The Gypsies of Spain. The Bible in Spain* was almost univerwally praised by the critics — who found Borrow's later, semi-autobiographical novels such as *Lavengro* and *The Romany Rye* too rough for Victorian sensibilities. It remained for the less genteel twentieth century to decide that these later works have special riches of their own. *The Bible in Spain* is now available in two editions in Great Britain and one in the United States.

LORNA DOONE

Richard Blackmore's (1825–1900) *Lorna Doone,* now being published in many editions by fourteen publishers in Great Britain and eleven in the United States, was first published in 1869, when it attracted little interest for a year and a half. Then, according to Kunitz and Haycraft's *British Authors of the Nineteenth Century,* people decided that it must be connected with the family of the Marquis of Lorne, who had just married a daughter of Queen Victoria — and its success was assured.

BOB, SON OF BATTLE

Alfred Ollivant's (1874–1927) *Bob, Son of Battle,* with one edition in print today, became a cult in the United States almost as soon as it was published by Doubleday and McClure in 1898. *The Bookman* writes (1898) of it, "We admire this book extremely for several reasons – for its originality, for its virile and expressive English, above all for its grit . . . its sentiment is never flabby. . . ." The English edition, entitled *Owd Bob,* was neglected for ten years before it came into its own. The relatively recent motion picture of this book, *To The Victor,* starring Willie Fyffe, has enjoyed popularity both in Great Britain and in the United States.

THE MAN ON THE BOX

Harold MacGrath's (1871–1932) *The Man on the Box* is, for some reason, currently available in a nine-dollar reprint of the 1904 original, which was copyrighted by the Bobbs-Merrill Company and sold at $1.50. This highly successful romance in its dramatized form was performed 123 times in New York, with Henry E. Dixey as the star. MacGrath, who began his writing career as a reporter for the Syracuse, N.Y., *Herald,* wrote such successful early silent film serials as *The Perils of Pauline.*

MRS. WIGGS OF THE CABBAGE PATCH

Mrs. Rice's (1870–1942) *Mrs. Wiggs,* which may be secured today in two editions in the United States and one in England, sold 200,000 copies in the first three years after it was published by the Century Company in 1901. It was dramatized, filmed, transcribed in Braille, and translated into French, German, Swedish, Danish, Chinese, and Japanese. For it and her other successful works Mrs. Rice "claimed no more...than that they appealed to the same kind of people about whom they were written" (Kunitz and Haycraft's *Twentieth Century Authors).* The success of her books allowed Mrs. Rice to found the Cabbage Patch Settlement house in her home city, Louisville, Ky.

WHEN KNIGHTHOOD WAS IN FLOWER

Charles Major's (1856–1913) *When Knighthood Was in Flower,* out of print today, tied for first place with Winston Churchill's *Richard Carvel* on the "best seller" lists of 1898, when the Bowen-Merrill Company brought it out. The book sold 200,000 copies in two years. Julia Marlowe starred in Paul Kester's dramatization of the story, and Marion Davies starred in the silent film version of 1922 — as Mary Pickford was to star in another Charles Major favorite, *Dorothy Vernon of Haddon Hall.*

CRANFORD

Elizabeth Gaskell's (1810–1865) *Cranford,* available today from one publisher in the United States and nine in Great Britain, can hardly be listed among successes-of-the-moment. From its first appearance in 1851 in the magazine *Household Words,* edited by Charles Dickens, and its publication in book form in 1853 by Chapman and Hall, it has remained the favorite among Mrs. Gaskell's writings and a strong favorite among Victorian novels in general. Its success has tended to overshadow such novels of social inquiry and protest as Mrs. Gaskell's *Mary Barton* and *Ruth,* which are only now being re-examined and re-assessed for their penetrating comments upon the problems of Victorian England.

T. TEMBAROM

Frances Hogdson Burnett's (1849–1924) *T. Tembarom,* out of print today, was a best seller when the Century Company published it in 1913 (after serializing it in the *Century Magazine*), despite such patronizing comments as that made by Frederic Tabor Cooper in *The Bookman:* "One sees Mrs. Burnett saying, 'I think I will rewrite *Little Lord Fauntleroy* for grown-up readers.' " Mrs. Burnett is said (Kunitz and Haycraft's *Twentieth Century Authors*) to have written one book over many times — a book which "made her rich, kept her happy, and brought joy to

millions of simple souls." Among these simple souls is your
editor.

THE SPENDERS

Harry Leon Wilson's (1867–1929) *The Spenders,* now out of
print, was published by Lothrop Publishing Company, Boston, in
1902. So successful was it that one month after its publication
the publishers gave Wilson a two-thousand-dollar advance which
encouraged him to resign as editor of the humor magazine *Puck*
and devote his time to the writing of such later successes as
Ruggles of Red Gap and *Merton of the Movies. The Spenders* was
dramatized by William H. Crane in 1903, and Crane starred as
Uncle Peter Bines in the dramatic version as successfully as he had
in *David Harum.*

OLDTOWN FOLKS

Harriet Beecher Stowe's (1811–1896) *Oldtown Folks* may now
be purchased in a fifteen-dollar reprint, or if you prefer the bargain edition Harvard University Press has a version available at
$9.50. The book, first published in 1869 by Fields, Osgood, and
Company of Boston, was in its twenty-eighth edition by 1885,
even though Mrs. Stowe's phenomenal success with *Uncle Tom's
Cabin* had made that novel the all-time favorite among her works.
Mrs. Stowe herself thought *Oldtown Folks* her best work, saying
"it is my résumé of the whole spirit and body of New England."
The recent attention to the work by critics and in scholarly edi-
tions suggests that the critics have come to agree with the author.

THE LITTLE MINISTER

James Barrie's (1860–1937) *The Little Minister,* available in
three editions in the United States, is, oddly enough, out of print
in Great Britain. Perhaps this fact is not odd, after all, since
twentieth-century British critics and readers have turned more
savagely on the sentimental in the work of their own nineteenth-
century writers than have outsiders — just as Americans have

turned upon sentimental American tales of an earlier era. Barrie's *Auld Licht Idylls* (1888) and *A Window in Thrums* (1889) had already made the young Scottish freelance journalist, working very hard in London, something of a celebrity before *The Little Minister*, published by Cassell in 1891, and by Lovell in the United States the same year, established him as a leading literary figure of his day. The romance was also serialized in the magazine *Good Words*. In 1897 Barrie himself dramatized the story, in the opinion of many critics considerably improving the plot. The play was an immediate success both in London and in New York. It is said to have made over eighty thousand pounds during the first ten years of its life in the theater. The success of *The Little Minister* in dramatic form turned Barrie's thoughts from novels to plays. He subsequently produced such favorites as *The Admirable Crichton*, *What Every Woman Knows*, *Dear Brutus*, and the perennial favorite, *Peter Pan*.

BESIDE THE BONNIE BRIER BUSH

In the same publishing season (1894) in which "Ian Maclaren's" (John Watson's, 1850–1907) *Beside the Bonnie Brier Bush* was brought out, Hardy's *Jude the Obscure* appeared. While the Hardy novel was receiving attention from a somewhat select circle of readers, the Maclaren book was selling a quarter of a million copies in Great Britain and half a million in the United States. By December 14, 1895, a Pittsburgh bookseller was writing to the *Publishers' Weekly* complaining that a cheap, incomplete, pirated edition of *Beside the Bonnie Brier Bush* was ruining business for the authorized edition, and declaring that Dodd, Mead and Company (United States publishers of the authorized edition) ought to do something about the situation. Despite the great success of this and other collections of Scottish stories by "Maclaren," the Reverend John Watson, very able and highly successful clergyman of the Free Church of Scotland, never allowed his writing of fiction to interfere with his ministerial duties at Sefton Park Church in Liverpool. In 1896 he delivered the Lyman Beecher lectures at Yale University, and received an honorary doctor of divinity degree from Yale. *Beside the Bonnie Brier Bush*, a slighter work than Barrie's similar *Auld Licht Idylls*, is out of print today.

IN HIS STEPS
The story of the fate of the Reverend Charles M. Sheldon's (1857–1946) *In His Steps* is now legendary, if not almost mythical. That story has been told in the note preceding the chapter from the book which is included in this anthology. It only remains to say that the Reverend Mr. Sheldon, like the Reverend Mr. Watson, was a dedicated and industrious clergyman despite his literary fame. In his case, because of faulty copyright provisions, he received only a few hundred dollars from the sale of his book — and, he tells us, about nine hundred letters weekly, for a time, asking for part of his immense earnings from the book to aid in this or that good work. The book is available today in three editions in the United States and one in Great Britain.